SPROUTS
BOOK 1:
PRENATAL CARE, DELIVERY, POSTPARTUM EXPECTATIONS, AND MENTAL DEVELOPMENT

INSTRUCTOR'S MANUAL

"IT TAKES A LOT OF LOVING TO GROW LITTLE SPROUTS."

ARISE Foundation, Order Toll-Free: 1-888-680-6100, Copyright © 1996-2009

260 LIFE MANAGEMENT LESSONS

Once shared as families sat around the kitchen table.

"Life-skills are not hereditary, they must be taught."
Susan and Edmund F. Benson, ARISE Founders

www.ariselife-skills.org

ITEM ID: SP1MW

COPYRIGHT

Special imprints, messages, and excerpts can be produced to meet your needs. For more information, contact us.

Order Toll-Free: 1-888-680-6100

www.ariselife-skills.org

SPROUTS:
PRENATAL CARE, DELIVERY, POSTPARTUM EXPECTATIONS, AND MENTAL DEVELOPMENT

TABLE OF CONTENTS

Go to www.ariselife-skills.org for fresh, vital lessons that connect youth emotionally and socially.

TABLE OF CONTENTS (cont.)

ARISE Foundation Order Toll-Free: 1-888-680-6100, Copyright © 1996-2009

ABOUT THE SPROUTS SERIES

Relationships today may not last as long as a good pair of sneakers. More than ever, young people need to wait and think before they decide to have children. They need a complete picture of exactly what's involved in having a child.

For those teenagers who have little ones out of wedlock, we want to provide information they desperately need in order to care for their children and raise them to be resilient, productive, and motivated individuals in our society.

Each book in the SPROUTS series deals with a different phase of pregnancy as well as child and family development. From prenatal care to reading to your youngster, this is a guide for those who are (we hope) years away from parenting. ARISE Life Management Skills interactive material has proven it stimulates participation and helps build better lives for tomorrow's children.

The Bensons

TIPS FOR TEACHING
ARISE LIFE MANAGEMENT SKILLS

You are about to undertake a real challenge: trying to change a human being's behavior and way of thinking. We refer to students as "learners" in our books.

Over the years, we have found the following tips very helpful in teaching ARISE Life Management Skills:

1. Be energetic. The livelier and more enthusiastic you are, the more involved learners will be.

2. Pay attention to learners' reading levels. Match your language to them and avoid commenting on their spelling or grammar.

3. Be positive. Make certain that learners' experience with you and this program is one of success. Praise them at every possible turn, even if their responses are inappropriate. Say things like:

4. Every opinion is valuable and any answer, no matter how off the wall, demonstrates the youth is paying attention. So praise *all* efforts. The objective of ARISE Life Management Skills is for everyone to participate and absorb the material.

5. Be kind. Never lecture to learners. Rather, *explain* to them. Talk with the group. Listen patiently.

6. Make yours an active class. Move around from time to time. Encourage the group to take part in role-playing, dramatizing stories, developing skits and songs, and all other ARISE Life Management Lessons.

7. Research by industrial training professionals indicates that people retain information better when they hear it rather than read it; and when they hear and see it, the retention rate improves by 40%. And, when we stand up and read, the mind works even better. So, to put it all together, when you want to really recall something you are reading, *read out loud while standing up.*

BEFORE CLASS

Things to do and say as your class begins:
• Explain how the class will operate. Stress that this program is interactive. Learners will be expected to participate fully through brainstorming, role-playing, discussion, and other activities.

DURING CLASS

As you instruct, remember:
• Learners will form small groups of three or four for some activities. Remember to mix them up; don't always place the same people together. For other exercises, they will be in pairs. Pair the more active participants with the less responsive ones. Keep in mind that youth learn from their peers and when they are interacting with each other.

• Do the worksheets together by reading the questions out loud. They will brainstorm to come up with answers.

• With quizzes, make sure the instructions you give are clear and complete. Read the quiz questions to everyone.

AFTER CLASS

As you reach the end of the class, do the following:
• Ask the group what they got out of the session each day. Encourage feedback. Find out what else they would like to learn about this subject.

Go to www.ariselife-skills.org for fresh, vital lessons that connect youth emotionally and socially.

ADDITIONAL TIPS FOR TEACHING ARISE LIFE MANAGEMENT SKILLS

① YOU FAMILIARIZE YOURSELF WITH THE LESSON BEFORE CLASS.

② YOU INTRODUCE YOURSELF AND HAVE LEARNERS DO THE SAME.

③ YOU BEGIN BY DISCUSSING GOALS OF THIS LESSON.

④ YOU MAKE EVERYONE FEEL THAT THIS IS ONE OF THE MOST VALUABLE EXPERIENCES OF THEIR LIVES.

⑤ YOU MOVE AROUND THE GROUP ASKING FOR OPINIONS AND PRAISING LEARNERS' CONTRIBUTIONS.

⑥ YOU UNDERSTAND SOME LEARNERS HAVE DIFFICULTY WITH SPELLING, PUNCTUATION AND VERBAL SKILLS SO YOU HELP AND ENCOURAGE THEM.

⑦ YOU CLOSE BY RESTATING THE ACTIVITIES' GOALS AND COMPLIMENTING THE GROUP FOR THEIR PARTICIPATION.

PERFORMANCE EVALUATION

This program is not based on how well young people learn the answers to quizzes. Rather, this program is considered successful when learners have participated fully and enthusiastically in class. When they have learned to think a little differently ... when they have enjoyed being part of the program.

In order to assess learners' participation, observe them during class. Record your observations as soon as possible while your recollections are fresh. Use a notepad to record what you observe.

How to observe:

- Focus your observation on a few learners at a time.
- Observe learners at the beginning of class, during class, and at the end of class.
- Observe learners when they are working as individuals, as a partner, or as part of a group.

What to observe:

- Observe which learners understand new concepts.
- Observe which learners need extra support.
- Observe which learners contribute to conversation or activity.
- Observe which learners interact with classmates, and how they interact.

What you will gain through observation:

- How to identify learners' strengths.
- How to recognize areas that need improvement.
- How to set goals together in areas that need to be developed.
- How to provide needed feedback to learners themselves.
- How to make recommendations to other adults involved in the learners' lives.

Go to www.ariselife-skills.org for fresh, vital lessons that connect youth emotionally and socially.

SPROUTS:
PRENATAL CARE, DELIVERY, AND POSTPARTUM EXPECTATIONS

SECTION ONE

> *"We find delight in the beauty and happiness of children that makes the heart too big for the body."*
> — *Ralph Waldo Emerson*

www.ariselife-skills.org

ARISE Foundation, Order Toll-Free: 1-888-680-6100, Copyright © 1996-2009

<table>
<tr><td>

1

</td><td>

PRENATAL CARE

Objective: Learners will develop an awareness of the importance of prenatal care, including visits to the doctor, good nutrition, and general health care.

</td></tr>
</table>

PRENATAL POEM
Worksheet: *Page 50*   **Learner's Workbook:** *Page 4*

1.   Ask learners to define "prenatal." Explain prenatal means what happens to a pregnant woman and her baby before the child is born. During this time, it is important for expectant mothers to take especially good care of themselves to prevent possible problems with pregnancy.

2.   Have participants open their workbooks to worksheet page 50, Learner's Workbook page 4. Allow time to create a poem about keeping healthy during pregnancy. For example, *eating a balanced diet, getting regular exercise, and going for routine doctor check-ups.*

3.   Once everyone has finished, encourage them to present their work out loud.

DOCTOR VISITS
Worksheet: *None*

1.   Discuss how important it is for a woman to see a doctor as soon as she thinks she may be pregnant. Prenatal visits give expectant mothers the opportunity to ask questions. They can talk about changes their bodies are going through and discuss physical discomforts and methods of relief.

2.   Divide learners into pairs and have them talk about any problems future mothers may experience (physical or emotional). For example, *they may feel insecure about raising a child, or perhaps gaining weight is a big issue.*

3.   Share responses as a group. Add the following answers if they are not mentioned: *feeling tired, headaches, dizziness, nausea, vomiting, cramps (leg, abdomen, back), heartburn, varicose veins, belching, constipation, blotching of the skin, swelling of hands, feet, or hemorrhoids.*

Go to www.ariselife-skills.org for fresh, vital lessons that connect youth emotionally and socially.

SHARE AND DISCUSS THE FOLLOWING WITH LEARNERS:

Worth Remembering...

When I was pregnant, I obsessed about whether my baby would be okay. What soothed me most was finally hearing her heartbeat.

— Melanie Haiken, *Parenting Magazine*

Go to www.ariselife-skills.org for fresh, vital lessons that connect youth emotionally and socially.

SHARING WHAT YOU KNOW
Worksheet: *Page 51*   **Learner's Workbook:** *Page 5*

1. Inform participants that doctors usually perform blood tests to check for conditions such as Rh factor, anemia, Rubella (German measles), and sexually transmitted diseases like HIV. These are done to ensure a healthy baby.

2. Explain to learners Rh factor is a substance found in a person's red blood cells. When a woman who's Rh-negative becomes pregnant, it's very important to determine whether or not her child carries the Rh factor. This is crucial because a mother who has this condition will develop antibodies in her blood which destroy her baby's red blood cells. There is a chance Rh-positive infants born to Rh-negative mothers may have anemia, jaundice, or brain damage. The youngster may even die. Doctors have been able to reduce these risks by giving the woman a medication called Rhogam, which prevents the mother's blood from developing those antibodies that attack her infant's blood cells.

3. Direct everyone to worksheet page 51, Learner's Workbook page 5. Have participants write a letter to a pregnant friend convincing her to get tested.

SEXUALLY TRANSMITTED DISEASES
Worksheet: *None*

1. Herpes and syphilis are two STDs (sexually transmitted diseases) expectant mothers need be especially concerned about. Symptoms of genital herpes include: *a rash, minor sores or large blisters, open sores on the genitals or anal area.* This disease is easily passed on to someone else. It's also possible to have herpes and not show any signs. The first warning of syphilis is an open sore called a chancre (pronounced SHANK-er). It can be located on the genitals of both men and women, inside the vagina, anal area, mouth, or throat.

2. Women with herpes cannot deliver a baby vaginally because the infant may catch the disease during childbirth. If the disease is in an active stage, a mother will have a cesarean section (a C-section), in which her stomach is cut open to deliver the child. It is very important to prevent herpes infection in newborns because if the disease is left untreated, the baby will die.

3. Teach learners that prevention is the best medicine. While condoms help to stop the spread of STDs, they are not foolproof. Ask volunteers to discuss different steps they will take to protect themselves against herpes and syphilis.

ARISE Foundation, Order Toll-Free: 1-888-680-6100, Copyright © 1996-2009

QUESTIONS FOR THE DOCTOR

Worksheet: *Page 52*　　　　**Learner's Workbook:** *Page 6*

1.　Explain to learners how important it is for a pregnant woman to ask her doctor any questions she may have. Direct everyone to worksheet page 52, Learner's Workbook page 6. Select volunteers to read each question. Have them check the boxes next to those they feel are most important.

2.　Discuss the role-play as a group. *Is there anything else the group would ask?*

WHAT MAKES ME NERVOUS

Worksheet: *Page 53*　　　　**Learner's Workbook:** *Page 7*

1.　Have each person turn to worksheet page 53, Learner's Workbook page 7. Ask them to list any concerns or worries they may feel about pregnancy. For example: *Am I going to be a good mother? Will I ever be thin again? Is it going to hurt a lot when I have a baby?*

2.　Encourage learners to share their thoughts with the group.

SERVICE AGENCY LIST; WHERE TO GO FOR HELP

Worksheet: *Pages 54-57* **Learner's Workbook:** *Page 8-11*

1.　Inform members there are many places a pregnant woman can turn for help. Have them look at worksheet pages 54-57, Learner's Workbook pages 8-11. Ask participants to read each situation and decide which agency to contact for aid and guidance.

2.　Discuss answers together. *Are there other organizations not included on this list?*

SHARE AND DISCUSS THE FOLLOWING WITH LEARNERS:

The U.S. Public Health Service provides a free 24-hour hotline to answer questions and inform the public where the nearest testing center for the HIV virus is located.

Call 1-800-342-AIDS for more information.

WHAT'S TO EAT?
Worksheet: *Page 58*   **Learner's Workbook:** *Page 12*

1. Ask learners: *How important do you think nutrition is to an expectant mother? Should she eat a lot of candy, potato chips, and red meat? Why or why not?*

2. Inform them good nutrition is very important for a mother-to-be and her child. Explain it's a great idea for pregnant women to keep track of what they eat. Encourage participants to brainstorm some ways to do this. For example, *keep a log of what they have at every meal.*

3. Distribute worksheet page 58, Learner's Workbook page 12. Have everyone answer the questions. Once all have finished, instruct volunteers to share their answers with the group.

HEALTHY FOOD GUIDE
Worksheet: *Pages 59-64* **Learner's Workbook:** *Pages 13-18*

1. Before planning a nutritious meal, we have to know about healthy food choices. The Food Pyramid is a good place to start. It lists different types of foods and how much of each is best.

2. Have everyone look at worksheet pages 59-64, Learner's Workbook pages 13-17. Select a person to read each section of the Food Pyramid. Do the same for pages 60-64, Learner's Workbook pages 14-17. (Explain each item listed on the Healthy Food Guide equals one serving. For example, *in the grain products group, 1/2 cup oatmeal equals one serving.)*

3. Direct participants to worksheet page 65, Learner's Workbook page 18. Have them plan one day's menu using both the Food Pyramid and Healthy Food Guide worksheets. Review and discuss their work as a group.

4. Instruct learners to compare their answers from What's to Eat with Building a Daily Menu. Ask for volunteers to answer the following: *What foods should you eat more often? Which ones should you have less of?*

DAILY NUTRITION CHECKLIST
Worksheet: *Page 65*   **Learner's Workbook:** *Page 19*

1. Have everyone go to worksheet page 65, Learner's Workbook page 19. Explain this will help them keep track of exactly what they eat.

2. Ask learners to take the lists home and check off each time they have a certain food.

Go to www.ariselife-skills.org for fresh, vital lessons that connect youth emotionally and socially.

ARISE Foundation, Order Toll-Free: 1-888-680-6100, Copyright © 1996-2009

FUTURE MOM ALERT!
Worksheet: *None*

1. Inform learners expectant mothers should avoid certain foods and substances.
   Choose volunteers to read the following tips.

   - Pregnant women must check with their doctor before using "home remedies."
   - A woman's body needs some salt when she is pregnant, but care must be taken not to overdo it.
   - Cheese, peanut butter, yogurt, fruit, and vegetables are good healthy snacks for an expectant mother. Candies, pastries, chips, and sweet drinks have a lot of calories but few vitamins or minerals.
   - Mothers-to-be should drink six to eight glasses of water every day.
   - Caffeine is found in tea, coffee, soft drinks (sodas) and chocolate; too much is not safe for an unborn baby.
   - **Smoking during pregnancy is linked with serious problems in newborns.**
   - **Women who drink while pregnant risk giving birth to a child with a condition known as Fetal Alcohol Syndrome (FAS). FAS infants require medical treatment.**

2. As a group, discuss any questions participants may have regarding these tips.

Foods to Avoid
Worksheet: *Page 66*   **Learner's Workbook:** *Page 20*

1. Explain how consuming certain food or drinks during pregnancy increases the chances of birth defects and other health problems. Expectant mothers must avoid all alcoholic beverages, products containing caffeine (including chocolate), sweets (cookies, cakes), saturated fats (fried foods), and most red meats.

2. Have members turn to worksheet page 66, Learner's Workbook page 20. Encourage participants to circle foods they should avoid while pregnant.

3. Discuss answers as a group once everyone has finished.

SHARE AND DISCUSS THE FOLLOWING WITH LEARNERS:

Very few babies in the United States (about five percent) arrive on their actual due date. Ten percent are born late (after 42 weeks) and 11 percent are premature (before 37 weeks).

Go to www.ariselife-skills.org for fresh, vital lessons that connect youth emotionally and socially.

Folic Acid

Worksheet: *Page 67*   **Learner's Workbook:** *Page 21*

1. Foods containing a mineral called folic acid help protect an unborn baby against a birth defect of the spine and brain known as spina bifida or "open spine." Some acids found in asparagus, broccoli, orange juice, and beans also decrease the risk of heart disease. Sometimes, it's hard to get important minerals through diet alone, so many doctors give pregnant women a vitamin to make sure they get enough.

2. Have the group open their books to worksheet page 67, Learner's Workbook page 21. Once everyone completes the worksheet, ask for volunteers to share some recipes with foods containing this ingredient.

Iron and Calcium

Worksheet: *Page 68*   **Learner's Workbook:** *Page 22*

1. Inform learners it is necessary for a pregnant woman to eat plenty of foods containing vitamins and minerals, especially iron and calcium. Iron is good for the blood and prevents anemia (a condition in which the blood is deficient in red blood cells), while calcium helps build strong bones and teeth.

2. Direct everyone to worksheet page 68, Learner's Workbook page 22. Have a volunteer read the list out loud.

3. Ask members to make a three-minute presentation on how an expectant mother can make sure she gets enough of these in her diet. For example, *eat a salad every day or remember to drink milk.*

SHARE AND DISCUSS THE FOLLOWING WITH LEARNERS:

Worth Remembering...

The first three months felt like a never-ending case of bad indigestion. My doctor suggested taking antacids, so I crunched TUMS all day long. At least it boosted my calcium.

— Victoria Von Biel, *Parenting Magazine*

TOO MUCH SUGAR
Worksheet: *Page 69* **Learner's Workbook:** *Page 23*

1. Explain to learners too much sugar is not good for anyone's diet, especially a pregnant woman's. It is turned into fat by the body and can cause tooth decay and cavities. Diabetes (too much sugar in the blood), can create serious problems for the baby and mother.

2. Have everyone open to worksheet page 69, Learner's Workbook page 23. Explain names listed on the worksheet are other words for sugar.

3. Discuss with participants what an expectant mother could do to cut down on this substance. Share answers as a group. Some responses may include *not eating sweets and giving up sodas.*

FAT ALERT
Worksheet: *Page 70* **Learner's Workbook:** *Page 24*

1. Inform learners a woman must watch the amount of fatty foods she eats during her pregnancy. Eating too much can raise blood pressure, blood sugar levels, cholesterol, and fats in the blood. It may also prevent an expectant mother from having a normal delivery.

2. Have everyone turn to worksheet page 70, Learner's Workbook page 24. Ask for a volunteer to read the high-fat meals on the left and another to recite the low-fat choices on the right.

3. Encourage participants to brainstorm ways a mother-to-be can reduce fat in her diet. For example, *staying away from cheeseburgers and French fries.*

RECIPES

Worksheet: *Pages 71-75*   **Learner's Workbook:** *Pages 25-29*

1.   Have participants look at worksheet pages 71-75, Learner's Workbook pages 25-29. Direct learners to take these worksheets home and practice using the recipes to make healthy meals.

SAMPLE PREGNANCY MENU

Worksheet: *Page 76*   **Learner's Workbook:** *Page 30*

1.   Inform participants the diet of a pregnant woman should consist of 2,200 calories per day. Have everyone look at worksheet page 76, Learner's Workbook page 30. Discuss why this daily menu is a good one for an expectant mother. Some answers may be: *she's getting what she and the baby need to be healthy or it doesn't include a lot of fatty foods.*

EXERCISE IS NECESSARY

Worksheet: *None*

1.   Explain to learners when you're pregnant, exercise (upon doctor's approval) is important to stay in shape and good health. Ask participants to suggest some activities they could do. If no one mentions the following, share these with them:

  ● Walking, swimming, or riding a bike (these help prevent varicose veins and increase circulation to the legs)
  ● Climbing short stairways or using a step machine (works out the legs)

2.   Divide participants into groups of four. Ask them to create and act out a skit about working out during pregnancy.

SHARE AND DISCUSS THE FOLLOWING WITH LEARNERS:

Alcohol is the No. 1 cause of preventable retardation and mental birth defects in newborns.

SUBSTANCE ABUSE: ALCOHOL

Worksheet: *Page 77*   **Learner's Workbook:** *Page 31*

1.   Discuss with learners how substance abuse during pregnancy not only harms the mother, but her unborn baby as well.

2.   Let each person look at worksheet page 77, Learner's Workbook page 31. Ask a volunteer to read it to the group.

3.   Select two people to role-play a concerned friend and a pregnant woman who wants a drink. The "friend" must convince the other person this is not a good idea.

4.   Discuss the example as a group. *Did her reasons not to drink sound convincing? What would you have said instead?*

SUBSTANCE ABUSE: CAFFEINE

Worksheet: *Pages 78 and 79*   **Learner's Workbook:** *Pages 32 and 33*

1.   Direct everyone to worksheet page 78, Learner's Workbook page 32. Encourage volunteers to read it out loud.

2.   Discuss with learners the negative effects of caffeine. Ask them to share why it's unhealthy for a pregnant woman to consume a lot of this. *Did they know drinking coffee or soda could harm their babies?* Talk about their opinions on this topic.

3.   Have members go to worksheet page 79, Learner's Workbook page 33. After everyone has finished, share answers as a group. *(Answers are on page 190 of this Manual.)*

SUBSTANCE ABUSE: CIGARETTES

Worksheet: *Pages 80 and 81*   **Learner's Workbook:** *Pages 34 and 35*

1.   Request members turn to worksheet pages 80 and 81, Learner's Workbook pages 34 and 35. Select a volunteer to read it out loud.

2.   Divide learners into two groups: one will be pro-smoking, the other against it. They should debate (positively argue) their positions on this subject. Have participants use the worksheets for this discussion.

Go to www.ariselife-skills.org for fresh, vital lessons that connect youth emotionally and socially.

Substance Abuse: Drugs
Worksheet: *Pages 82 and 83*   **Learner's Workbook:** *Pages 36 and 37*

1. Ask someone to read worksheet page 82, Learner's Workbook page 36.

2. Select two volunteers to role-play the following: Your pregnant friend did drugs before she found out she was expecting a baby. Convince her to stop using them and get help for her addiction.

3. Discuss the role-play as a group.

4. Direct learners to worksheet page 83, Learner's Workbook page 37. *(Answers are on page 190 of this Manual.)* Once they have finished, encourage volunteers to discuss problems they or their loved ones have had with drugs.

Substance Abuse Poster
Worksheet: *Page 84*   **Learner's Workbook:** *Page 38*

1. Have everyone turn to worksheet page 84, Learner's Workbook page 38. Encourage participants to design a poster showing the effects drugs, alcohol, or smoking have on unborn children. Suggest they create these in groups and display them.

Caring Pregnancy
Worksheet: *Page 85*   **Learner's Workbook:** *Page 39*

1. Inform learners pregnant women need to take good care of themselves. They should relax and put their feet up as often as possible and avoid stress and tiring activities.

2. Divide participants into groups of four. Have them flip to worksheet page 85, Learner's Workbook page 39. Ask them to come up with 10 ways for a woman to take it easy during this time. For example: *take a bath every night and nap throughout the day.*

3. Share and discuss answers with everyone.

SIGNS OF TROUBLE
Worksheet: *Page 86*   **Learner's Workbook:** *Page 40*

1. Explain to participants how problems may occur during pregnancy. Have each person go to worksheet page 86, Learner's Workbook page 40. If an expectant mother has any of these symptoms, she must call her doctor right away.

2. Ask for three volunteers to role-play what they would do if they were pregnant and experienced these dangerous signs. Answers may include: *phone a relative or friend or call 911 for help if no one is around.*

GESTATIONAL DIABETES
Worksheet: *Pages 87 and 88*   **Learner's Workbook:** *Pages 41 and 42*

1. Talk about how approximately three to five percent of all women in the United States develop gestational diabetes (high blood sugar levels) during pregnancy. The American Diabetes Association recommends testing for this disease between the 24th and 28th week. In order to do this, an expectant mother is asked to drink a liquid containing 50 grams of glucose. One hour later, a blood sample is drawn. If the level is too high, an additional test called a glucose tolerance test (this takes three hours), must be done.

2. Tell learners gestational diabetes can develop in the second half of pregnancy. Proper nutrition and exercise are important to keep it under control. Diet, exercise, and insulin can be used to keep blood glucose levels normal.

3. Inform participants some signs of this condition include dizziness, fatigue (being tired), extreme thirst, sweating, frequent urination, and blurred vision. If a woman experiences any of these symptoms, she must contact her doctor at once.

4. Have everyone look at worksheets pages 87 and 88, Learner's Workbook pages 41 and 42. Ask volunteers to read the information to the group.

5. Encourage them to share changes they think an expectant mother must make in her life to follow these guidelines.

Go to www.ariselife-skills.org for fresh, vital lessons that connect youth emotionally and socially.

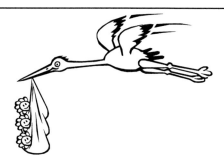

Foods to Avoid Crossword Puzzle
Worksheet: *Pages 89 and 90*   **Learner's Workbook:** *Pages 43 and 44*

1. Have everyone turn to worksheet pages 89 and 90, Learner's Workbook pages 43 and 44. Ask participants to fill in names of foods pregnant women with gestational diabetes should avoid.

2. As a group, discuss any comments or questions learners may have. *(Answers are on page 190 of this Manual.)*

Food Guide
Worksheet: *Pages 91 and 92*   **Learner's Workbook:** *Pages 45 and 46*

1. Inform learners the food guide for a pregnant woman with gestational diabetes differs from the one other expectant mothers should follow. Someone with this condition needs to be even more careful about the amount of fat and sugar she eats.

2. Direct members to worksheet page 91, Learner's Workbook page 45. Select volunteers to read information to the group.

3. Have each person go to worksheet page 92, Learner's Workbook page 46. Let them draw a line from the food group on the left to the item belonging to the group on the right.

4. Discuss together. *(Answers are on page 190 of this Manual.)*

Diabetes Menu
Worksheet: *Page 93*   **Learner's Workbook:** *Page 47*

1. Have learners look at worksheet page 93, Learner's Workbook page 47. Ask for volunteers to read the sample menu to the group.

2. Select two volunteers to role-play a doctor and a pregnant woman who has gestational diabetes. The "doctor" must explain the diabetes menu to the person and why it's important she follow it.

3. Discuss the role-play with the group. *Did the doctor convince his patient to watch what she eats? What would you have done differently?*

DIABETES DANGERS

Worksheet: *Page 94*   **Learner's Workbook:** *Page 48*

1.   Inform learners if a pregnant woman is not careful, gestational diabetes can cause problems for both her and the unborn child. Have everyone turn to worksheet page 94, Learner's Workbook page 48. Ask volunteers to read this information to the group.

2.   Ask participants to comment on the worksheet. *Does this scare them? Will they try to take better care of themselves?*

Letter to My Future Child

Worksheet: *Page 95*   **Learner's Workbook:** *Page 49*

1.   Have learners flip to worksheet page 95, Learner's Workbook page 49. Challenge them to write letters to their future children on how they plan to be good parents. Encourage participants to express their fears and excitement, as well as a plan for providing their little ones with the best life possible.

Wrap-Up: Key Tips

Worksheet: *Page 96*   **Learner's Workbook:** *Page 50*

1.   Review worksheet page 96, Learner's Workbook page 50 with learners and discuss it as a group.

Instructor: It's time again...give your group the quiz (page 97 of this Manual and page 51 of the Learner's Workbook) before going on to the next chapter. (Answers are on page 194 of this Manual.)

2

DELIVERY

Objective: Learners will develop an awareness of delivery procedures.

DELIVERY VOCABULARY LIST; DELIVERY DEFINITIONS
Worksheet: *Pages 98-100*   **Learner's Workbook:** *Pages 52-54*

1. Direct everyone to worksheet pages 98 and 99, Learner's Workbook pages 52 and 53. Select someone to read each definition. Discuss them as a group. *Did they ever hear these words before?*

2. Have each person turn to worksheet page 100, Learner's Workbook page 54. Inform learners these delivery terms are helpful to know.

3. Select volunteers to read each item on the worksheet. Complete the activity together and review answers with participants. *(Answers are on page 190 of this Manual.)*

PREGNANCY WORD SEARCH
Worksheet: *Page 101*   **Learner's Workbook:** *Page 55*

1. Have members turn to worksheet page 101, Learner's Workbook page 55. Encourage them to fill in the blanks and find words in the puzzle.

2. Discuss answers as a group. *(Answers are on page 190 of this Manual.)*

SCRAMBLED DELIVERY
Worksheet: *Page 102*   **Learner's Workbook:** *Page 56*

1. Make sure all turn to worksheet page 102, Learner's Workbook page 56. Have participants use words on the vocabulary list to solve and unscramble those on the worksheet.

2. Review answers together. *(Answers are on page 190 of this Manual.)*

ARISE Foundation. Order Toll-Free: 1-888-680-6100, Copyright © 1996-2009

DELIVERY, POSTPARTUM, AND INFANT NEEDS
Worksheet: *Pages 103-105*   **Learner's Workbook:** *Pages 57-59*

1. Inform learners there are several items an expectant mother needs to have ready for her hospital stay and at home for a newborn.

2. Explain giving birth and taking care of a baby is much easier when parents are properly prepared. Have everyone look at worksheet pages 103-105, Learner's Workbook pages 57-59. On worksheet page 105 and Learner's Workbook page 59, ask them to write various items from the list in the correct place.

3. Encourage participants to discuss how they will get money to purchase things they will need for their babies when the time comes to start a family.

IMAGINE YOUR DELIVERY
Worksheet: *Page 106*   **Learner's Workbook:** *Page 60*

1. Ask learners to imagine what the delivery routine for a pregnant woman is like. Then, select volunteers to read the following tips from your book on making the last stage much easier:

    - Several weeks before an expectant mother is due, she should check with her hospital about touring the areas where she will be a patient. For example, she could visit the delivery area, recovery room, and surgical area (should a C-section be necessary).
    - Pregnant women must ask many questions of their doctors, childbirth educators, and hospital staff about what's going to happen after they arrive.
    - It's a good idea for expectant parents to preregister at the hospital so they won't have to think about it later. This way, they can complete all of the paperwork in advance and the father won't have to leave while his partner is in labor to complete the necessary forms.
    - It's very important to prepare an emergency contact card and post it in a visible spot.
    - Expectant mothers should stay mobile (take walks) during early labor to reduce discomfort, ease back pain, and allow gravity to assist their labor. They must check with their doctor to see how much movement is allowed once checked into the hospital.
    - Pregnant women must know how they will get to the hospital and who will take them. Necessary arrangements must be made before they go into labor.
    - If the mother has other children, she must figure out who will help with child care while she's at the hospital.

2. Direct everyone to look at worksheet page 106, Learner's Workbook page 60. Have participants imagine what a delivery day in their futures will be like and write about it. Some answers may include: *being nervous, feeling very happy, or suffering.*

3. Share responses as a group.

Go to www.ariselife-skills.org for fresh, vital lessons that connect youth emotionally and socially.

EMERGENCY CONTACT CARD
Worksheet: *Page 107*   **Learner's Workbook:** *Page 61*

1. Inform learners how important it is to be prepared for an emergency. Pregnant women, especially, must keep a list of phone numbers handy in case there's a problem.

2. Have participants turn to worksheet page 107, Learner's Workbook page 61. Ask them to complete the information and keep it for easy reference.

MY PERFECT BABY SHOWER
Worksheet: *Page 108*   **Learner's Workbook:** *Page 62*

1. Ask learners to look into the future and imagine what their baby showers will be like. *Are there a lot of games, presents, and guests?* Have them share their visions with the group.

2. Direct everyone's attention to worksheet page 108, Learner's Workbook page 62. Encourage participants to create a plan for their future parties. Remind them to use the Delivery, Postpartum, and Infant Needs worksheets to write their gift wish lists as well as names of people they'd like to invite.

3. Share their plans as a group. *Where would they have it? How many will attend?*

SHARE AND DISCUSS THE FOLLOWING WITH LEARNERS:

> # *Worth Remembering...*
>
> *I think of birth as the search for a larger apartment.*
>
> — Rita Mae Brown, *Starting from Scratch*

Am I in Labor?

Worksheet: *Page 109*   **Learner's Workbook:** *Page 63*

1.   Instruct learners how it's not easy for a pregnant woman to tell whether or not she is going into labor. Explain that a woman may feel contractions throughout pregnancy as her body prepares itself for delivery. This is known as "false" labor.

2.   Select volunteers to read out loud these signs of "true" and "false" labor. (They will need to use your book.)
      In true labor, contractions usually...
      ● feel the same on either side. They begin at the cervix and move up and around to the back or begin at the lower back and move front.
      ● occur in a regular pattern. Those that average one minute in length, are approximately five minutes apart, and are very strong and painful indicate a woman may be in labor.
      ● grow longer, stronger, and more frequent.
      ● do not stop if a woman changes her activity.
      ● are not affected by drinking a glass of water.

      In false labor, contractions...
      ● begin in front and may not move back.
      ● may become longer or stronger.
      ● don't follow a regular pattern in most cases.
      ● will usually stop if a woman changes her activity.
      ● may stop if the woman drinks water.

3.   Divide group members into pairs. Make sure everyone turns to worksheet page 109, Learner's Workbook page 63. Discuss the two categories listed on top of the page; symptoms of labor are listed at the bottom. Have each person complete the page.

4.   Once all are done, review answers together.

Common Delivery Procedures

Worksheet: *Page 110*   **Learner's Workbook:** *Page 64*

1.   Share with learners how certain steps must be taken before an infant is born to make sure delivery goes smoothly. Both mother and baby have to be prepared for this special event.

2.   Ask everyone to flip to worksheet page 110, Learner's Workbook page 64. Discuss various steps usually performed before the birth. Have a different volunteer read each one.

3.   Encourage participants to make a short three-minute presentation on any fears or concerns they may have about future childbirth. Some answers may include: *Will I be in a lot of pain? Can I be a good parent?*

Go to www.ariselife-skills.org for fresh, vital lessons that connect youth emotionally and socially.

ORDER OF DELIVERY

Worksheet: *Page 111*   **Learner's Workbook:** *Page 65*

1.   Divide learners into groups of four. Instruct everyone to turn worksheet page 111, Learner's Workbook page 65. Encourage each one to brainstorm the order in which delivery steps occur.

2.   After all have finished, review responses together. *(Answers are on page 190 of this Manual.)*

WRAP-UP: KEY TIPS

Worksheet: *Page 112*   **Learner's Workbook:** *Page 66*

1.   Review worksheet page 112, Learner's Workbook page 66 with learners and discuss it as a group.

Instructor: It's time again...give your group the quiz (page 113 of this Manual, Learner's Workbook page 67) before going on to the next chapter. (Answers are on page 194 this Manual.)

<table>
<tr><td>**3**</td><td></td></tr>
</table>

POSTPARTUM EXPECTATIONS

*Objective: Learners will develop an awareness
of postpartum symptoms and expectations.*

CHANGES IN MY LIFE
Worksheet: *Page 114*   **Learner's Workbook:** *Page 68*

1.   Ask participants to imagine what will happen if they have a baby. Have
     volunteers share how they think their lives would change.

2.   Direct each person to turn to worksheet page 114, Learner's Workbook page 68.
     Have them write all the changes they might experience when they bring a new baby
     home from the hospital.

3.   Discuss answers with the group.

POSTPARTUM MISCONCEPTIONS
Worksheet: *Page 115*   **Learner's Workbook:** *Page 69*

1.   Inform learners "postpartum" is a period of physical and emotional change that occurs during the
     first six to eight weeks a woman gives birth.

2.   Make sure everybody looks at worksheet page 115, Learner's Workbook page 69. Ask volunteers
     to read the statements and let them place a "T" or "F" next to each.

3.   Share responses as a group. *(Answers are on page 191 of this Manual.)*

SHARE AND DISCUSS THE FOLLOWING WITH LEARNERS:

Worth Remembering...

*Now the thing about having a baby —
and I can't be the first
person to have noticed this — is that
thereafter you have it.*

— Jean Kerr, *Please Don't Eat the Daisies*

Go to www.ariselife-skills.org for fresh, vital lessons that connect youth emotionally and socially.

POSTPARTUM SYMPTOMS
Worksheet: *Pages 116 and 117*   **Learner's Workbook:** *Pages 70 and 71*

1. Discuss how a woman's body goes through many changes during pregnancy and she should not expect it to return to normal right after giving birth. Share these physical symptoms mothers can expect during the first few weeks after returning home from the hospital: *bloody vaginal discharge, exhaustion, discomfort when sitting, difficulty with urination and bowel movements, general soreness, heavy sweating, and breast discomfort.* Ask learners to discuss how much time and effort they think a mother should devote to getting back in shape.

2. Direct participants to worksheet page 116, Learner's Workbook page 70. Ask several volunteers to read it out loud. Then instruct them to use the worksheet in deciding if a doctor should be called in each situation on worksheet page 117, Learner's Workbook page 71.

3. Share responses as a group.

SHARE AND DISCUSS THE FOLLOWING WITH LEARNERS:

Several medical organizations, including the American Academy of Pediatrics, recommend a baby be breast-fed for the first six months of life.

NEW PARENT SURVIVAL TIPS
Worksheet: *Page 118*   **Learner's Workbook:** *Page 72*

1. Talk with the group about how new parents can be easily stressed by their new responsibilities. It's important for them to relax and pace themselves.

2. Have everyone look at worksheet page 118, Learner's Workbook page 72.

3. Ask volunteers to discuss how a new parent can accomplish each tip.

NEW PARENT STRESS MANAGEMENT
Worksheet: *Page 119*   **Learner's Workbook:** *Page 73*

1. Inform learners any change in one's life creates stress, and a new baby is a big change. Discuss how using support systems like family and friends is a wonderful way for parents to cope.

2. Direct everyone to look at worksheet page 119, Learner's Workbook page 73. Ask them to create a list of trusted relatives and friends whom they would feel comfortable asking for help. Once they have done this, have each person use the key at the bottom of the page to describe different kinds of support they can get from each individual.

3. Have them share with the group the person they will most likely turn to for help when a new baby enters their lives. Encourage participants to explain why this person is so important to them.

12 TIPS TO GET A GRIP; SUPPORT YOURSELF
Worksheet: *Pages 120 and 121*   **Learner's Workbook:** *Pages 74 and 75*

1. Remind learners how important it is for parents to control their temper and handle anger. Have each person look at worksheet page 120, Learner's Workbook page 74. Explain this list is good to keep around the house in case they need help managing their tempers.

2. Ask for volunteers to read the list and act out the steps.

3. Direct all to worksheet page 121, Learner's Workbook page 75. Have participants imagine they are new parents. Instruct them to write a letter of support to themselves using tips from the worksheet.

WHAT TO DO WITH ANGER
Worksheet: *Page 122*   **Learner's Workbook:** *Page 76*

1. Discuss with learners how most anger comes from fear and by getting rid of fear they can eliminate anger. Inform participants to ask themselves what they are scared of whenever they feel mad. If they're dealing with another person, suggest that instead of thinking "What a terrible person," they ask themselves, "What is he afraid of?"

2. Ask members go to worksheet page 122, Learner's Workbook page 76. Have them place an "X" on those boxes containing good ways of dealing with anger.

3. Review answers as a group.

Go to www.ariselife-skills.org for fresh, vital lessons that connect youth emotionally and socially.

A LETTER TO MY PARTNER
Worksheet: *Page 123*   **Learner's Workbook:** *Page 77*

1. Instruct learners even though a woman carries a baby and gives birth, the child is not created without the mother's partner. The father of the infant needs to be involved in the youngster's life in order for him to grow up healthy.

2. Ask all participants to look at worksheet page 123, Learner's Workbook page 77. Have everyone write a note to his partner about what is expected of him once an infant is born.

3. Select volunteers to stand up and share their letters with the group.

4. Encourage a group discussion on the part fathers play in nurturing and raising a little one. Let participants talk about the mental, physical, and financial support dads must provide.

SETTING GOALS, MANAGING TIME
Worksheet: *Pages 124 and 125* **Learner's Workbook:** *Pages 78 and 79*

1. Inform learners new parents must learn how to manage time wisely to avoid burnout. Once they know what is needed to care for their babies and still have some time for themselves, child-raising becomes a little bit easier. In fact, everyone could use a good way to organize their daily activities.

2. Explain to members a good tip for parents (or anyone else, for that matter) is to make a list of all that needs to be done and then assign each item an "A," "B," or "C" in order of importance. A's are urgent, "must-do" items; B's are important, but not serious; C priorities are of lesser importance.

3. Have all participants flip to worksheet page 124, Learner's Workbook page 78. Ask them to use this chart to make a list of all the things they need to do in the upcoming week and place them in either the A, B, or C column. When two A priorities collide and there's not enough time in the day, learners need to negotiate (bargain) with those involved to create a workable compromise. By using this ABC method, nothing is forgotten and you are always in control. Direct everybody to update the list each evening so when they wake in the morning, they'll be up and running without wasting time. Stress how important it is to take time to enjoy their accomplishments and then update their ABC goals for the next day.

4. Ask each person to turn to worksheet page 125, Learner's Workbook page 79. Allow learners to think about things in their lives they feel are priorities and assign them A, B, or C in order of importance. Remind them to set dates for completion.

5. Request several people to share their ideas for organizing time once they have a family. Have them discuss goals as a group.

Go to www.ariselife-skills.org for fresh, vital lessons that connect youth emotionally and socially.

ARISE Foundation, Order Toll-Free: 1-888-680-6100, Copyright © 1996-2009

ORGANIZING SPACE
Worksheet: *Page 126*   **Learner's Workbook:** *Page 80*

1. Inform learners an organized space makes caring for an infant much easier. Ask them to tell you what things new parents need at the changing table. Some examples include: *diapers, powder, lotion, nail clippers, cotton balls, clothes, and baby wipes.* Remind participants that if there are other small children around the house (or once an infant is able to get around on his own), parents must securely lock all medicine above adult shoulder height.

2. Have participants go to worksheet page 126, Learner's Workbook page 80. Instruct them to make a list of materials parents need in the changing area.

3. Share and discuss answers as a group.

BABY RAP
Worksheet: *None*

1. Ask participants to say why they think it's important to organize time effectively to raise a healthy, happy baby.

2. Divide learners into groups of four. Have each team create a rap about smart ways to manage time.

3. Allow each one to perform their rap for everyone.

SHARE AND DISCUSS THE FOLLOWING WITH LEARNERS:

Women who exercise have lower levels of stress and depression.

Go to www.ariselife-skills.org for fresh, vital lessons that connect youth emotionally and socially.

Baby at Home Crossword Puzzle
Worksheet: *Pages 127 and 128*   **Learner's Workbook:** *Pages 81 and 82*

1. Direct everyone to complete worksheet pages 127 and 128, Learner's Workbook pages 81 and 82.

2. Once all participants have finished, share answers as a group. *(Answers are on page 191 of this Manual.)*

Wrap-Up: Key Tips
Worksheet: *Page 129*   **Learner's Workbook:** *Page 83*

1. Review worksheet page 129, Learner's Workbook page 83 with learners and discuss tips together.

Instructor: It's time again...give your group the quiz (page 130 of this Manual, Learner's Workbook page 84) before going on to the next chapter. (Answers are on page 194 of this Manual.)

TALK SHOW

Objective: Learners will develop an awareness of the dangers of taking drugs and smoking during pregnancy by role-playing a talk show.

TALK SHOW

Worksheet: *Pages 131-138*   **Learner's Workbook:** *Pages 85-92*

1.   Before the activity, explain to learners they will be given an opportunity to learn valuable information about substance abuse during pregnancy through role-playing a talk show.

2.   Define the following talk-show roles:

   a.   Host: Greets guests, asks questions of members, walks through audience, selects who will stand up and question the panel, keeps issues flowing, and makes the talk show entertaining. Must be enthusiastic at all times.

   b.   Panel members: Individuals featured as the talk-show guests address the show's topic. Each will be given a different stand to take with regard to the subject.

   c.   Audience: Provide cheers when they agree with the panel's point of view. Certain members (selected in advance) will stand up and ask specific questions. Others may also raise their hands and, if selected by the talk-show host, offer their point of view on the topic.

3.   After discussing the roles, select volunteers for each of the parts.

4.   Have everybody look at worksheet pages 131-137, Learner's Workbook pages 85-91 and hand one to each of the panel members in the role-play. Allow time to review the positions they will represent and ask if they have any questions. Remind them to use information on the role cards as background; they should still add their own "touch" to the part and expand on what's provided.

5.   Ask everyone to tear out and distribute one question per learner from worksheet page 138, Learner's Workbook page 92. Explain selected people will ask these of the panel once they have completed their roles. When they finish preparing, signal host to begin the show.

6.   Remind them the show should only take about 15 minutes. Once finished, discuss the skit as a group. *Have participants ever experienced situations like this? If yes, what did they do?*

SPROUTS:
MENTAL DEVELOPMENT

SECTION TWO

www.ariselife-skills.org

ARISE Foundation, Order Toll-Free: 1-888-680-6100, Copyright © 1996-2009

YOUR CHILD'S MENTAL DEVELOPMENT

Objective: Learners will understand how they can help turbocharge their child's mind and stimulate a youngster's mental development.

MIND POWER

Worksheet: *Page 142*   **Learner's Workbook:** *Page 96*

1. Have learners turn to worksheet page 142, Learner's Workbook page 96. Select one volunteer to read the information.

2. As a group, discuss why it is important to give a young child attention, as well as the opportunity to grow up in an exciting environment and develop his mind power.

MENTAL DEVELOPMENT TABLE

Worksheet: *Pages 143 and 144*   **Learner's Workbook:** *Pages 97 and 98*

1. Direct participants to look at worksheet pages 143 and 144, Learner's Workbook pages 97 and 98. Ask for volunteers to read the information and discuss each different stage as a group.

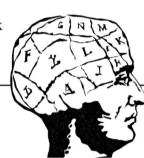

SHARE AND DISCUSS THE FOLLOWING WITH LEARNERS:

Worth Remembering...

Don't forget when compared to a grown-up, every baby is a genius. Think of the capacity to learn! The freshness, temperament, and will of an infant a few months old!

— May Sarton, *Mrs. Stevens Hears the Mermaids Singing*

Go to www.ariselife-skills.org for fresh, vital lessons that connect youth emotionally and socially.

A SMARTER BABY
Worksheet: *Page 145*　　　　**Learner's Workbook:** *Page 99*

1.　Direct participants to worksheet page 145, Learner's Workbook page 99. Ask them to select an age (newborn to three years old.) Have them write it on top of the page and develop a plan to provide a child in this age group with activities to develop his mind power.

BABY TALK
Worksheet: *Page 146*　　　　**Learner's Workbook:** *Page 100*

1.　Have learners turn to worksheet page 146, Learner's Workbook page 100 and inform them each situation shows parents involved in an activity with a child. Ask participants to fill in what each could be saying. The first one has been done as an example.

2.　Encourage everyone to act out their dialogues.

STIMULATE YOUR CHILD
Worksheet: *None*

1.　Inform each person how important it is to give their child stimulation. Encourage volunteers to suggest interesting situations where their babies will want to hold up their heads and use their eyes. Discuss ideas as a group. These could include *give him something interesting to look at or put him on a blanket so he sees you moving about.*

SHARE AND DISCUSS THE FOLLOWING WITH LEARNERS:

Play some soft music to calm and soothe a crying infant; it will relax him and provide the parent with a much-needed "breather."

Go to www.ariselife-skills.org for fresh, vital lessons that connect youth emotionally and socially.

ARISE Foundation, Order Toll-Free: 1-888-680-6100, Copyright © 1996-2009

VALUE OF PEEK-A-BOO
Worksheet: *None*

1.   Explain to learners how important it is for babies to know people are still there even though you sometimes can't see them. Parents can teach this to their little ones by playing a simple game of "peek-a-boo" or talking to the child while they are in another room.

2.   Encourage participants to think of ways to train infants and toddlers to understand this fact. An example may be *putting a teddy bear in the closet and closing the doors; explain to the youngster it is still there, just out of sight.*

SAFE SPACE
Worksheet: *Page 147*   **Learner's Workbook:** *Page 101*

1.   A young child learns much through movements, but these should not be limited any more than is necessary for his physical safety. For example, the youngster should not be wrapped too tightly in a blanket or strapped to a chair or bed unless it is for very short periods of time or safety reasons.

2.   Have each learner flip to worksheet page 147, Learner's Workbook page 101. Direct them to draw a picture of a child's physical space where he spends most of his time and describe how it is kept safe while still allowing the youngster room to move around. Remind everyone the idea is to combine these two things.

WAYS TO TREAT YOUR CHILD
Worksheet: *Page 148*   **Learner's Workbook:** *Page 102*

1.   Have everyone turn to worksheet page 148, Learner's Workbook page 102. Ask them to read the statements and indicate if they are proper or improper practices.

2.   Direct learners to share responses with the group. Remind them to explain why improper actions are not good for the mental development of infants and how they could correct them. Explain to participants that parents who give youngsters attention, love, and affection are turbocharging their child's emotional development and mind power.

MAKING CHOICES
Worksheet: *Page 149*   **Learner's Workbook:** *Page 103*

1. It is important to help children learn to make decisions on their own. This can be frustrating for a youngster when he has too many choices. For example, it may be difficult to select what he wants for dinner; deciding between chicken fingers or macaroni could be less frustrating.

2. Direct participants to worksheet page 149, Learner's Workbook page 103. Ask them to explain which decisions are easy or hard for little ones to make. As a group, have learners rewrite the difficult ones so they become more child-friendly. For example, the question is: *What would you like for lunch?* To make it more specific, you could ask: *Would you like ham or turkey on your sandwich?*

FINGER PLAYS
Worksheet: *Page 150*   **Learner's Workbook:** *Page 104*

1. Have everyone turn to worksheet page 150, Learner's Workbook page 104. Explain how finger plays, songs, and poems all teach young children valuable language skills.

2. Ask for volunteers to perform some of the finger plays for the group. *Which one was the best? Why?*

COMPLETE THE RHYME
Worksheet: *Page 151*   **Learner's Workbook:** *Page 105*

1. Inform learners nursery rhymes are an important way to teach young children language skills. Ask participants to look at worksheet page 151, Learner's Workbook page 105. Have them unscramble the words to complete each rhyme. *(Answers are on page 192 of this Manual.)*

DRESS-UP TRUNK
Worksheet: *Page 152*   **Learner's Workbook:** *Page 106*

1. Talk with participants about the many things children learn through imitation. Parents can help develop this skill by providing youngsters with safe dress-up material. These could include clothes, necklaces, and shoes.

2. Have learners flip to worksheet page 152, Learner's Workbook page 106 and ask them to choose items from home which could be used. Some examples are *an old hat, coat, or pair of sunglasses.* Direct them to write these on the worksheet and share with the group.

Do It Yourself
Worksheet: *Page 153*   **Learner's Workbook:** *Page 107*

1. Explain to learners teaching their child how to carefully hold materials and equipment will help him handle quite a number of tasks. Then, have everyone turn to worksheet page 153, Learner's Workbook page 107.

2. Select a volunteer to read the first two examples. Encourage participants to think of ways they can plan other learning experiences for little ones.

Teach a New Skill
Worksheet: *Page 154*   **Learner's Workbook:** *Page 108*

1. Small children usually work at slower speeds and need to repeat tasks often. It is important parents do not force a youngster to try a new activity if he isn't interested. They must also be ready to give the child help when needed. When teaching a toddler new skills, plan them out as teaching exercises, then break them down into small, simple steps.

2. Direct learners to worksheet page 154, Learner's Workbook page 108. Encourage them to select a skill to teach, divide it into small steps, then write down each of those actions. An example may be teaching your child to fold clothes. First, you would tell him to get together all the laundry he is going to fold. Then, take each piece of clothing and fold it in half, then in half again. Make sure they are all in a neat pile and ready to be put away.

3. Next, have everyone select a partner and read directions to him. They should do only what is said. Suggest each person check how well the instructions were written and how his partner was able to follow them. *Was this hard to do? For which person? Why?*

Cooking With Kids
Worksheet: *Page 155*   **Learner's Workbook:** *Page 109*

1. Instruct group members that cooking with children provides an excellent learning opportunity. It teaches many things: life skills, math, reading, socialization (getting along with others), and following directions.

2. Have each person turn to worksheet page 155, Learner's Workbook page 109. Ask participants to read the information and plan an imaginary cooking lesson they feel comfortable doing with a two or three year old.

3. Encourage volunteers to share their ideas with everyone, describe what's on the menu, and explain how the child will help. Remember to follow the safety tips.

LIFE LEARNING
Worksheet: *Page 156*   **Learner's Workbook:** *Page 110*

1. Discuss how any moment can be learning time with young children since they are so eager to soak up new information. Direct learners to open to worksheet page 156, Learner's Workbook page 110. Have them read each of the situations and ask how parents could teach these through daily activities. The first one has been done as an example.

2. Encourage each person to share their responses with the group.

KIDS AND TV
Worksheet: *Page 157*   **Learner's Workbook:** *Page 111*

1. Have participants turn to worksheet page 157, Learner's Workbook page 111. Ask for a volunteer to read the information out loud.

2. Divide everyone into two groups. Tell them one will take the point of view that youngsters should watch limited amounts of TV; the other will argue that children should be able to watch as much TV as they want. Select a person from each group to debate (a positive argument). After the first two have completed their discussions, encourage two other people to present their views. *Whose argument was the best? Why?*

QUALITY TELEVISION
Worksheet: *Page 158*   **Learner's Workbook:** *Page 112*

1. Have learners flip to worksheet page 158, Learner's Workbook page 112. Direct each person to watch a children's television show and write a report summarizing (selecting the main points) the program and why they thought it was good or bad. Instruct them to use the worksheet to help organize their reports.

2. Once finished, discuss participants' work as a group.

Choosing TV Programs
Worksheet: *Page 159*   **Learner's Workbook:** *Page 113*

1. Talk with learners about different ways to choose good television programming for children. Have them look at worksheet page 159, Learner's Workbook page 113. Ask participants to fill out the worksheet based on the show they watched for the previous activity.

2. Discuss answers as a group.

TV Tips Secret Code
Worksheet: *Page 160*   **Learner's Workbook:** *Page 114*

1.   Have everyone look at worksheet page 160, Learner's Workbook page 114. Inform learners these tips are all written in code. Encourage them to decode each letter and discover ways to help their child deal with television in a healthy manner. *(Answer is on page 192 of this Manual.)*

Wrap-Up: Key Tips
Worksheet: *Page 161*   **Learner's Workbook:** *Page 115*

1.   Review worksheet page 161, Learner's Workbook page 115 with learners and discuss it as a group.

Instructor: It's time again...give your group a quiz (page 162 of this Manual, Learner's Workbook page 116) before going on to the next chapter. (Answers are on page 194 of this Manual.)

SHARE AND DISCUSS THE FOLLOWING WITH LEARNERS:

Worth Remembering...
The education a child receives from his parents the first four years of life is more significant than four years of college.

— Zig Ziglar, *Raising Positive Kids in a Negative World*

Go to www.ariselife-skills.org for fresh, vital lessons that connect youth emotionally and socially.

6   TOYS AND BOOKS

Objective: To give learners guidelines of suitable toys, books, and activities to ensure a mentally well-developed youngster.

SUITABLE TOYS AND ACTIVITIES
Worksheet: *Pages 163 and 164*   **Learner's Workbook:** *Pages 117 and 118*

1. Have each learner turn to worksheet pages 163 and 164, Learner's Workbook pages 117 and 118. Select volunteers to read the information out loud.

2. Discuss worksheets together. *What do they think of the information?*

CHOOSE THE APPROPRIATE TOY
Worksheet: *Page 165*   **Learner's Workbook:** *Page 119*

1. Direct participants to worksheet page 165, Learner's Workbook page 119. Have them use worksheet pages 163 and 164 or Learner's Workbook pages 117 and 118 and write the appropriate age range under each toy.

2. Share answers as a group.

Toys Around the House
Worksheet: *Page 166*   **Learner's Workbook:** *Page 120*

1. Explain to learners many items in the house are safe and can be used as toys for young children. Encourage them to look at worksheet page 166, Learner's Workbook page 120. Have them think of things in each of the rooms that could be used as safe playthings for little ones. One has been done as an example.

2. Select volunteers to suggest other items they feel are okay for toddlers.

ARISE Foundation, Order Toll-Free: 1-888-680-6100, Copyright © 1996-2009

BUBBLE RECIPE
Worksheet: *None*

1. Share with learners how bubbles are a great source of entertainment for children; parents can even share in the fun!

2. Inform participants they can make their own formulas at home with their kids. Write the following "bubble recipe" on a board or a large piece of paper where all can see:

    Mix: 3/4 cup tearless shampoo, 2 quarts water, 1 cup glycerine

3. Encourage them to write this recipe down, take it home, and prepare it with a little one.

SHARE AND DISCUSS THE FOLLOWING WITH LEARNERS:

> ### *Worth Remembering...*
>
> *When your child clearly identifies learning with loving, he will love learning.*
>
> — Zig Ziglar, *Raising Positive Kids in a Negative World*

IS IT SAFE?
Worksheet: *Page 167*   **Learner's Workbook:** *Page 121*

1. Toys cause more than 100,000 injuries to children each year. In selecting playthings, learners need to look for the following:

    *   sturdiness: beware of flimsy toys ready to fall apart; make sure eyes of stuffed animals are firmly attached
    *   safe finish: paint, coating
    *   secure construction: no small pieces, sharp edges, breakable parts
    *   washability: if toys can't be cleaned, they become breeding places for germs
    *   safe size: larger than baby's fist
    *   no strings attached: use plastic links to attach toys and objects

2. Have everyone turn to worksheet page 167, Learner's Workbook page 121. Ask participants to read each description and decide if it's safe for a child. Share responses and personal experiences as a group.

LIBRARIES
Worksheet: *None*

1.   Libraries are great places for the whole family. These centers offer many things to youngsters, including books, videotapes, films, and story times.

2.   Ask learners to look through a telephone book to locate the library nearest their homes. Participants will use it to plan interesting learning experiences for their children.

3.   If possible, invite a representative from the local library system to speak to group members.

4.   As a conclusion, have each person discuss the variety of free programming available for little ones.

Go to www.ariselife-skills.org for fresh, vital lessons that connect youth emotionally and socially.

Read To Your Child
Worksheet: *None*

1.   Inform participants the love of reading can lead to a world of pleasure. They can give this gift to their children by sharing a story with them every day.

2.   Ask for volunteers to tell the class a story they remember from childhood. If learners need help thinking of one, give them the following titles: *Goldilocks and the Three Bears, Three Billy Goats Gruff, Little Red Riding Hood, or Three Little Pigs.* Have participants use different voices for each character. *Which one was their favorite? Why? What did it teach them?*

CREATE A STORY
Worksheet: *Page 168*   **Learner's Workbook:** *Page 122*

1.   Explain some of the best tales for kids are those where youngsters are the stars. Have learners turn to worksheet page 168, Learner's Workbook page 122. Ask them to create a story in which a child encounters a problem and solves it. For example, *Joanna finds an injured kitten in the park near her home.*

ARISE Foundation, Order Toll-Free: 1-888-680-6100, Copyright © 1996-2009

Toys and Books Crossword Puzzle
Worksheet: *Pages 169 and 170*   **Learner's Workbook:** *Pages 123 and 124*

1.   Have learners complete worksheet pages 169 and 170, Learner's Workbook pages 123 and 124.

2.   After everyone has finished, review responses as a group. *(Answers are on page 192 of this Manual.)*

WRAP-UP: KEY TIPS
Worksheet: *Page 171*   **Learner's Workbook:** *Page 125*

1.   Review worksheet page 171, Learner's Workbook page 125 with learners and discuss it as a group.

SHARE AND DISCUSS THE FOLLOWING WITH LEARNERS:

Instructor: It's time again...give your group a quiz (page 172 of this Manual, Learner's Workbook page 126) before going on to the next chapter. (Answers are on page 194 of this Manual.)

ARISE Foundation Order Toll-Free: 1-888-680-6100, Copyright © 1996-2009

<table>
<tr><td>7</td></tr>
</table>

POETRY

Objective: Learners will understand the value of reading poetry to their child.

POEMS

Worksheet: *Pages 173-175*   **Learner's Workbook:** *Pages 127-129*

1. Discuss the value of poetry with learners. Explain that reading poems to children can be a rewarding experience for both parents and youngsters.

2. Have each person turn to worksheet pages 173-175, Learner's Workbook pages 127-129. Encourage volunteers to read out loud.

3. Ask if anyone recalls a poem from childhood. Share these as a group.

MY OWN POEM

Worksheet: *Page 176*   **Learner's Workbook:** *Page 130*

1. Direct participants to worksheet page 176, Learner's Workbook page 130. Have learners write a poem they will one day read to their children.

2. Ask for volunteers to stand up and read their creations out loud.

Worth Remembering...

Parents learn a lot from their children about coping with life.

— Muriel Spark, *The Comforters*

POETRY SECRET CODE

Worksheet: *Page 177*   **Learner's Workbook:** *Page 131*

1.   Have members flip to work page 177, Learner's Workbook page 131. Ask learners to decode the words to find a useful parenting tip.

2.   Once everyone has finished, discuss it as a group. *(Answer is on page 192 of this Manual.)*

WRAP-UP: KEY TIPS

Worksheet: *Page 178*   **Learner's Workbook:** *Page 132*

1.   Review worksheet page 178, Learner's Workbook page 132 with participants and talk about it as a group.

SHARE AND DISCUSS THE FOLLOWING WITH LEARNERS:

Parents must keep an eye on how much TV their children are watching. The following chart is a good guideline to use:

Age	TV Time
Birth to 18 months	Very little; 10 minutes at the most, whenever parent needs a short break.
18 months to two years	Half an hour, two to three times per week.
Two years	One hour of educational TV shows per day.

— Adapted from *Parenting Magazine,* June/July 1996

Instructor: It's time again...give your group a quiz (page 179 of this Manual, Learner's Workbook page 133) before going on to the next chapter. (Answers are on page 194 of this Manual.)

Go to www.ariselife-skills.org for fresh, vital lessons that connect youth emotionally and socially.

ARISE Foundation, Order Toll-Free: 1-888-680-6100, Copyright © 1996-2009

8

TALK SHOW

Objective: By role-playing a talk show, learners will understand how to stimulate a child's growth and imagination.

TALK SHOW

Worksheet: *Pages 180-186*　　**Learner's Workbook:** *Pages 134-140*

1. Before the activity, explain how each person will be given an opportunity to learn valuable information about developing a child's mental skills through role-playing a talk show.

2. Define the following talk-show roles:

   a. Host: Greets audience, welcomes the panel, selects several audience members to stand up, and asks questions. Also keeps issues flowing and makes the program entertaining. Must be enthusiastic at all times.

   b. Panel members: Individuals who are featured as talk-show guests to address show's topic. Each will be given a different stand to take with regard to the subject.

   c. Audience: Provide cheers when they agree with panel's point of view. Certain audience members (selected in advance) will stand up and ask questions. Others may also raise their hand and, if selected by the talk-show host, offer their views.

3. After discussing roles, select volunteers for each part.

4. Hand out cards on worksheet pages 180-184, Learner's Workbook pages 134-139 to each panel member in the role-play. Give learners time to review positions they will represent and ask questions they may have. Remind participants to use information contained on role cards as background; they should still add their own "touch" to the part and expand on what has been provided.

5. Photocopy worksheet page 185, Learner's Workbook page 140 and have learners cut or tear out one questions. When they finish preparing, signal host to begin the show.

6. Remind them the show should only take about 15 minutes. Once finished, discuss the skit as a group. *Have participants ever experienced situations like this? If yes, what did they do?*

SPROUTS:

SECTION ONE

PRENATAL CARE, DELIVERY, AND POSTPARTUM EXPECTATIONS

LEARNER'S WORKSHEETS

> *Soft is the heart of a child. Do not harden it.*
> — *Unknown*

www.ariselife-skills.org

Go to www.ariselife-skills.org for fresh, vital lessons that connect youth emotionally and socially.

PRENATAL POEM

On the lines below, create a poem about keeping healthy during pregnancy. For these purposes, don't worry about grammar or spelling. Just do the best you can. The main idea is for you to participate.

_____

_____

_____

_____

_____

_____

_____

_____

_____

ARISE Foundation. Order Toll-Free: 1-888-680-6100, Copyright © 1996-2009

SHARING WHAT YOU KNOW

Write a letter to a pregnant friend convincing her to get tested for HIV. In the note, use the information below. For these purposes, don't worry about grammar or spelling. Just do the best you can. The main idea is for you to participate.

Since 1991, more than 2,600 children in the United States younger than age 13 have developed AIDS.

Many children with AIDS were infected by their mothers during pregnancy or delivery.

Approximately 70 percent of newborns who test positive for HIV will test negative for the virus after several months. This is because of the time it takes for healthy newborns to get rid of maternal antibodies (things that fight off disease) from their systems.

Dear Friend,

_____

_____

_____

_____

_____

_____

Love,

_____

Go to www.ariselife-skills.org for fresh, vital lessons that connect youth emotionally and socially.

QUESTIONS FOR THE DOCTOR

❑ Are childbirth preparation classes available? What are the costs? When and where are they held?

❑ Whom should I call to discuss minor discomforts or problems?

❑ Which blood tests are routinely ordered? When will I know the results?

❑ How are medical visits scheduled? What are the office hours? Will the same doctor be seen at each visit?

❑ Which hospital do you suggest I use for delivery?

❑ What are the costs for prenatal care, blood tests, sonograms, and ultrasound screenings during my pregnancy?

❑ What financial arrangements can be made? If there is insurance coverage, how will payments be scheduled?

❑ What insurance coverage do you accept?

List any additional questions you may have for your doctor about pregnancy now or in the future.

_____

_____

_____

_____

WHAT MAKES ME NERVOUS

Below, write down any concerns or worries you have about pregnancy. For these purposes, don't worry about grammar or spelling. Just do the best you can. The main idea is for you to participate.

_____

_____

_____

_____

_____

_____

_____

_____

Go to www.ariselife-skills.org for fresh, vital lessons that connect youth emotionally and socially.

SERVICE AGENCY LIST

The following is a list of agencies a pregnant woman can turn to for help or answers about her pregnancy. Look in the Yellow, White, or Blue Pages of the phone book for local numbers and fill them in on the lines provided.

AIDS Hotline   _____

AL-ANON   _____
    (Help for families and loved ones of
    alcohol/drug abusers)

Alcoholics Anonymous   _____

Auto Safety Hotline   1-800-424-9393

Childhelp USA   1-800-4-A-CHILD (22-4453)
    (Child Abuse Hotline)

Mental Health Services   _____

Covenant House   1-800-999-9999
    (Crisis intervention, housing, and more)

County Public Health Unit   _____
    (AIDS, dental, disease prevention,
    mother and child care, primary care,
    immunizations)

Department of Children and Family Services   _____
    (Crime Relations Office, AFDC,
    Food Stamps, Medicaid)

Department of Youth and Family Development   _____
    (Family counseling, parent training)

ARISE Foundation. Order Toll-Free: 1-888-680-6100, Copyright © 1996-2009

SERVICE AGENCY LIST (cont.)

Child Support Enforcement Helpline   1-800-622-KIDS (5437)

Department of Children and Family Services   1-800-342-9152
    (Abuse, neglect, referrals)

Infant Screening Program   _____

Protective Services System   1-800-96-ABUSE (2-2873)

Hearing Help Line   1-800- EAR-WELL
    (327-9355)

Department of Children and Family Services   _____
    (Children's Medical Services —
    Chronic illness counseling for low-income
    families)

Department of Children and Family Services   _____
    (Children, Youth, and Families —
    Handles cases of child abuse)

La Leche League   _____
    (Support for breastfeeding mothers)

Narcotics Anonymous   _____

Parents Anonymous   1-800-352-LOVE (5683)

Planned Parenthood   _____
    (Pap smears, pregnancy tests, birth control)

Go to www.ariselife-skills.org for fresh, vital lessons that connect youth emotionally and socially.

Service Agency List (cont.)

Planned Parenthood Federation   of America   1-800-829-7732

Salvation Army Family Services   _____
    (Furniture, clothing, food, home-rental
    assistance)

Sudden Infant Death Syndrome   1-800-221-SIDS (7437)

Urban League Parent Assistance and Mobilization Center   _____
    (Housing, education, job training)

ARISE Foundation, Order Toll-Free: 1-888-680-6100, Copyright © 1996-2009

WHERE TO GO FOR HELP

In the spaces below, write down the name of the service agency where someone can turn for help.

Situation 1

Joanna has noticed her young daughter Stacy has several bruises on her legs. She knows Stacy has not fallen or bumped into anything. Joanna also has noticed her boyfriend Rick has become very mean to Stacy, yelling at her for no reason. She thinks Rick may be abusing her daughter. Who should she turn to for help?

_____

Situation 2

Kassandra has just been hired by a local engineering company and she needs to find a babysitter for her son David. Who could help her?

_____

Situation 3

Adriana gave birth to her daughter Nicole in January. It is now three months later and she is still feeling very depressed. The strains of motherhood are too much. Who should she turn to for help in dealing with her depression?

_____

Situation 4

Gloria decided to breast-feed her son Jose; however, she is worried he is not getting enough milk. Who could she talk to about breast-feeding?

_____

Go to www.ariselife-skills.org for fresh, vital lessons that connect youth emotionally and socially.

WHAT'S TO EAT?

Fill in the spaces below.

What did you eat or drink first
thing this morning?

_____

What did you eat next? Would you
consider it a snack or lunch?

_____

What did you have in the afternoon?

_____

For dinner?

_____

How many times per week do
you eat this same food?

_____

Do you munch on something after dinner
or before you go to bed?

_____

Do you eat alone or with someone
during any of your meals?

_____

Do you eat differently with family
or friends than by yourself?

_____

If yes, what do you have that's
not the same?

_____

ARISE Foundation. Order Toll-Free: 1-888-680-6100, Copyright © 1996-2009

HEALTHY FOOD GUIDE: THE FOOD PYRAMID

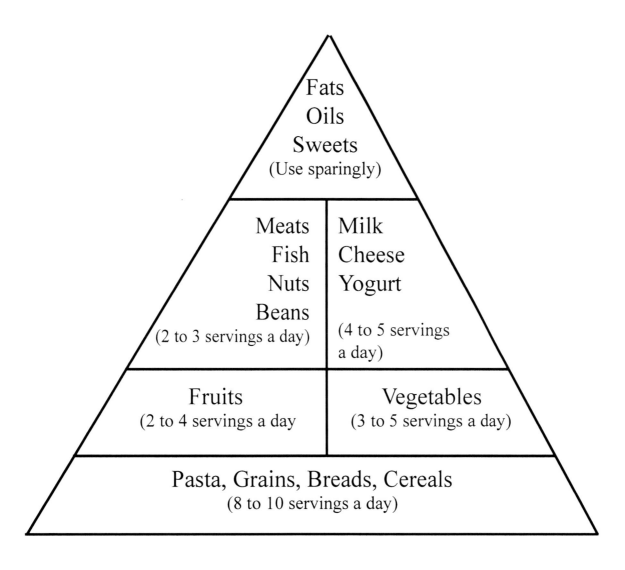

Fats
Oils
Sweets
(Use sparingly)

Meats
Fish
Nuts
Beans
(2 to 3 servings a day)

Milk
Cheese
Yogurt
(4 to 5 servings a day)

Fruits
(2 to 4 servings a day

Vegetables
(3 to 5 servings a day)

Pasta, Grains, Breads, Cereals
(8 to 10 servings a day)

Go to www.ariselife-skills.org for fresh, vital lessons that connect youth emotionally and socially.

HEALTHY FOOD GUIDE: RECOMMENDED SERVINGS

> Each item listed below equals one serving size. For example, six servings would be made up of: 1 slice of bread, 1 tortilla, 1 muffin, 4 crackers, 1/2 cup pasta, and 2 rice cakes.

GRAIN PRODUCTS: BREADS AND CEREALS (8 TO 10 SERVINGS DAILY)

Grain products provide energy, vitamins, and minerals. Look for whole grain breads, such as whole wheat bread. Limit pastries, doughnuts, and cookies because they contain lots of fat and sugar.

Choose these grain products:

1 slice whole grain bread
1/2 cup oatmeal, grits, or cooked wheat
1/2 cup rice (white or brown)
2 tortillas
1 muffin or biscuit
4 crackers
1/2 cup corn, potato, yuca, malanga, boniato

3/4 cup cereal
1 pancake or waffle
1/2 cup pasta
1/2 pita
1/2 bagel
2 rice cakes

> Each item listed below equals one serving size. For example, two oranges would equal two servings, since one whole orange is equal to one serving.

FRUITS (2 TO 4 SERVINGS DAILY)

Fruits provide vitamins and minerals. Limit drinks that contain added sugar. One-hundred-percent fruit juice has more of the vitamins you need.

Choose these fruits:

1 orange
1-1/4 cups cubed watermelon
1/2 small banana
1 guava
2 tablespoons dried fruit
1 peach
2 small tangerines

1/2 cup orange or grapefruit juice
3/4 cup strawberries
1 apple
1 mango
1 pear
1/2 cup pineapple
3/4 cup grapes

HEALTHY FOOD GUIDE: RECOMMENDED SERVINGS (cont.)

Each item listed below equals one serving size. For example, three servings of vegetables could be made up of: 1/2 cup squash and 1/2 cup eggplant.

VEGETABLES (3 TO 5 SERVINGS DAILY)

Vegetables provide vitamins and minerals. Fresh produce is best, but frozen or canned items are okay. Avoid fried foods.

Choose these vegetables:

1 cup Brussels sprouts
1/2 cup spinach
1 cup collard greens, kale, or cabbage
1/2 cup squash
1/2 cup green beans
1/2 cup sweet peas
1 medium tomato
1 cup broccoli

1/2 cup chopped green pepper
1/2 cup carrots
1/2 cup eggplant

Each item listed below equals one serving size. For example, 1 cup milk and 1 cup yogurt would equal two servings.

MILK AND MILK PRODUCTS: MILK, CHEESE, AND YOGURT (4 TO 5 SERVINGS DAILY)

Calcium builds bones and teeth. Coffee creamers and condensed milk have low nutritional value. If you can't digest the sugar in milk or are lactose-intolerant (allergic to dairy products), speak to your doctor about alternatives.

HEALTHY FOOD GUIDE: RECOMMENDED SERVINGS (cont.)

Choose these dairy products:

1 cup milk (whole, low fat, skim, powdered)

1 cup yogurt

1 cup cottage cheese

2 one-inch cubes of cheese

1 cup pudding or custard

1-1/2 cups soup made with milk

1 cup ice milk or ice cream (low-fat, low-sugar)

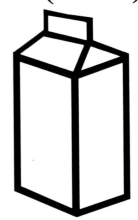

> Each item listed below equals one serving size. For example, 2 eggs, 1 cup tofu, and 2-3 ounces of lamb would equal three servings.

MEAT AND PROTEIN FOODS: MEAT, FISH, NUTS, AND BEANS (2 TO 3 SERVINGS DAILY)

Protein builds strong muscles and blood. Limit processed meats that are high in fat, such as hot dogs, bologna, sausage, spare ribs, turkey wings, and bacon.

Choose these meat and protein foods:

beef (2 to 3 ounces per serving)   lamb (2 to 3 ounces per serving)

pork (2 to 3 ounces per serving)   liver (2 to 3 ounces per serving)

chicken (2 to 3 ounces per serving)   turkey (2 to 3 ounces per serving)

fish (2 to 3 ounces per serving)   shellfish (2 to 3 ounces per serving)

2 eggs   1 cup baked beans

1 cup peas   1 cup tofu

1/2 cup peanut butter   1/2 cup nuts

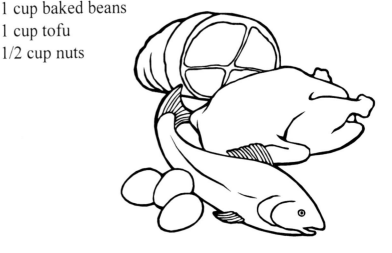

HEALTHY FOOD GUIDE: RECOMMENDED SERVINGS (cont.)

FATS, OILS, AND SWEETS (EAT IN LIMITED QUANTITIES)

The top of the food pyramid lists fats, oils, and sweets — products such as salad dressings and oils, cream, butter, margarine, sugars, sodas, candies, and sweet desserts. Limit your intake of these items.

HEALTHY FOOD GUIDE: BUILDING A DAILY MENU

Use the FOOD PYRAMID and the HEALTHY FOOD GUIDE: RECOMMENDED SERVINGS to plan a daily menu for yourself. For these purposes, don't worry about grammar and spelling. The main idea is for you to participate.

Breakfast

_____

_____

_____

Lunch

_____

_____

_____

Dinner

_____

_____

_____

Snacks

_____

_____

ARISE Foundation, Order Toll-Free: 1-888-680-6100, Copyright © 1996-2009

DAILY NUTRITION CHECKLIST

Post this checklist in your house and mark each food item as it is eaten. (The numbers refer to the recommended number of daily servings. For example, it is suggested that you eat a maximum of three servings per day from the milk, cheese, and yogurt group.)

1 2 3 4 5 6 7 8 9 10

Milk, cheese, yogurt	☐ ☐ ☐ ☐
Meat, poultry, fish, eggs, dried beans, nuts	☐ ☐ ☐
Fruits	☐ ☐ ☐ ☐
Vegetables	☐ ☐ ☐ ☐ ☐
Breads, cereals, rice, pasta	☐ ☐ ☐ ☐ ☐ ☐ ☐ ☐ ☐
Fats, oils, sweets	☐ ☐

Go to www.ariselife-skills.org for fresh, vital lessons that connect youth emotionally and socially.

FOODS TO AVOID

Circle foods to stay away from during pregnancy.

ARISE Foundation, Order Toll-Free: 1-888-680-6100, Copyright © 1996–2009

FOLIC ACID

Circle foods that contain folic acid.

IRON AND CALCIUM

Some foods high in iron are:

Oatmeal (cooked, without salt)

Cream of wheat

Rice (white, cooked)

Sirloin steak (broiled, lean)

Broccoli, spinach, all dark greens (cooked)

Peanuts (oil-roasted, unsalted)

All beans (cooked)

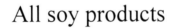

Tofu

All soy products

Some foods high in calcium are:

Skim milk

Yogurt (plain, low-fat)

All low-fat cheese

Broccoli, kale, collards, all dark greens

Peanuts (oil-roasted, unsalted)

Great Northern beans (cooked)

TOO MUCH SUGAR

Read each of the names below. **Remember:** they mean SUGAR!

Glucose: A simple sugar found in the blood.

Dextrose: Another name for glucose.

Fructose: Sugar found in fruit, juices, and honey.

Lactose: Sugar found in milk.

Maltose: Sugar formed by breakdown of starch.

Sucrose: Table sugar.

Granulated sugar: Sucrose.

Confectioner's sugar: Powdery sucrose.

Brown sugar: Sucrose crystals covered with a film of syrup.

Corn sugar: Sugar made from cornstarch.

Corn sweetener: Liquid sugar made from the breakdown of cornstarch.

Corn syrup: Syrup made by partial breakdown of cornstarch.

Honey: Syrup made up of mostly fructose.

Invert sugar: Combination of sugars found in fruits.

Maple syrup: Syrup made from sap of the sugar maple tree.

Molasses: Syrup separated from raw sugar during processing.

Mannitol: Sugar alcohol broken down and slowly absorbed by the body.

Sorbitol: Sugar alcohol more slowly absorbed than ordinary dietary sugar.

Sorghum: Syrup made from sorghum grain.

Barley malt: Syrup made from barley grain.

Rice syrup: Syrup made from brown rice.

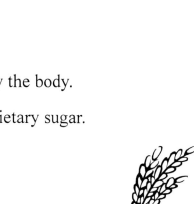

Go to www.ariselife-skills.org for fresh, vital lessons that connect youth emotionally and socially.

FAT ALERT

High-Fat Meals

	Amount	Calories	Fat Grams
Breakfast			
Croissant with egg, cheese, and sausage	1	523	38
Coffee	1 cup	5	0
Creamer	1 oz.	55	5
TOTALS		**583**	**43**
Lunch			
Sub shop ham and cheese (12" sub)	1	801	29
Mayonnaise	2 tbsp.	197	22
Mustard	2 tbsp.	36	2
Potato chips	2 bags	304	20
Regular soda	16 oz.	186	0
TOTALS		**1527**	**72**
Dinner			
Fried chicken with skin	1 breast	435	17
Mashed potatoes	1/2 cup	300	16
Salad	1 cup	10	0
Blue cheese dressing	2 tbsp.	119	12
Roll	1	83	1
Margarine	1 tsp.	34	4
Vegetables with butter	1/2 cup	39	3
Chocolate-chip cookie	1	120	7
Whole milk	1/2 cup	69	4
TOTALS		**1209**	**64**

Low-Fat Choices

	Amount	Calories	Fat Grams
Breakfast			
English muffin with butter	1 / 2 tsp.	189	6
Coffee	1 cup	5	0
Juice	12 oz.	153	0
TOTALS		**347**	**6**
Lunch			
Sub shop turkey (12" sub)	1	511	12
Lettuce and tomato	1	10	0
Mustard	2 tbsp.	36	2
Pretzels	2 bags	220	0
Orange juice	16 oz.	204	0
TOTALS		**981**	**14**
Dinner			
Roast skinless chicken	1 breast	284	6
Baked potato	1	200	2
Salad	1 cup	10	0
Fat-free dressing	2 tbsp.	45	0
Roll	1	83	1
Diet margarine	1 tsp.	17	2
Vegetable stir fry	1/2 cup	41	2
Fat-free fudge cookie	1	50	0
1% milk	1/2 cup	48	1
TOTALS		**767**	**15**

Go to www.ariselife-skills.org for fresh, vital lessons that connect youth emotionally and socially.

ARISE Foundation, Order Toll-Free: 1-888-680-6100, Copyright © 1996-2009

Sprouts: Prenatal Care, Delivery, Postpartum Expectations, and Mental Development, Page 70

RECIPES

Use these low-fat dips for vegetables, crackers, salad dressings, potato toppings, and as a substitute for mayonnaise and sour cream.

YOGURT-MUSTARD DIP

Ingredients:

1 cup nonfat yogurt
1 cup Dijon mustard
1/4 cup scallions or chives
2 tsp. herb seasoning

Directions:

Mix ingredients well.

BEAN DIP

Ingredients:

2 cups cooked or canned beans
1 tbsp. tahini (sesame paste)
1 clove garlic
2 tbsp. lemon juice
1 tsp. low-sodium soy sauce
1 tsp. dillweed
1 tsp. cayenne pepper
2 tbsp. parsley
2 tbsp. scallions
3 tbsp. water

Directions:

1. Rinse canned beans.

2. Place all ingredients in a food processor or blender. Blend for five minutes. Add water to make creamy.
3. Stuff into pita pocket with lettuce, tomato, and cucumbers for a vegetarian protein sandwich.

Go to www.ariselife-skills.org for fresh, vital lessons that connect youth emotionally and socially.

RECIPES (cont.)

HONEY-BASIL CHICKEN

Ingredients:

1 lb. skinless, boneless
   chicken breasts

Marinade:

1 cup raspberry vinegar
2 tbsp. low-sodium soy sauce
3 tbsp. Dijon mustard
2 tbsp. honey
2 tbsp. fresh basil, chopped
1 pinch black pepper
1/2 tsp. dried thyme

Servings: 4
Calories: 149
Fat: 4 g.

Directions:

1. Divide chicken into four portions. Combine marinade ingredients, add   chicken, and refrigerate for 15 minutes.

2. Spray cold grill with 100-percent vegetable oil. Heat coals until very hot and spray again just before adding poultry. Remove chicken from marinade and grill until cooked on each side.

3. Save marinade and place in a small pot. Simmer for five minutes.

4. To serve, pour marinade over chicken.

PASTA FAGIOLI

Ingredients:

1 tbsp. olive oil
1 large onion
3 cloves garlic, crushed
2 medium carrots, cut into thin slices
2 medium zucchini, sliced
2 tsp. dried basil
2 tsp. dried oregano

1 can (32 oz.) unsalted whole tomatoes
   (with liquid)
2 cans (16 oz. each) white canneloni or navy
   beans, drained and rinsed
3/4 lb. rigatoni or medium shells
Freshly ground black pepper

Go to www.ariselife-skills.org for fresh, vital lessons that connect youth emotionally and socially.

ARISE Foundation Order Toll-Free: 1-888-680-6100, Copyright © 1996-2009

RECIPES (cont.)

Directions:

1. Begin heating a large pot of water to cook pasta. Warm olive oil in a large skillet and cook onion and garlic, stirring occasionally until softened.

2. Add the carrots, zucchini, basil, oregano, tomatoes with their liquid, and beans. Cook until vegetables are tender (about 10 minutes). Season with pepper to taste.

3. While vegetables are cooking, boil pasta until tender but still firm (about seven minutes). Divide rigatoni or shells between eight plates and spoon the vegetables and sauce on top. Makes eight servings.

Per serving:

Calories:	335	**Carb.:**	63 g.
Fat:	3 g.	**Sodium:**	332 mg.
Protein:	14 g.		

HEARTWARMING MEATLESS CHILI

Ingredients:

1 tbsp. olive oil
3 large onions, chopped
3 cloves garlic, minced
4 cans (16 oz. each) kidney beans,
 drained and rinsed for one minute
(16 oz. each) unsalted whole pepper
 tomatoes, chopped
2 cans (8 oz. each) unsalted tomato sauce
2 tbsp. oregano

2 tsp. cumin
2 tsp. chili powder
Juice from 1/2 lemon
1/8 to 1/4 tsp. cayenne pepper
1/8 to 1/4 tsp. freshly ground black pepper
8 tsp. Cheddar or Parmesan cheese (optional)

Go to www.ariselife-skills.org for fresh, vital lessons that connect youth emotionally and socially.

RECIPES (cont.)

Directions:

1. Warm olive oil in medium skillet over moderate heat. Add onion and garlic and cook, stirring occasionally until softened. Add to a large pot along with kidney beans.

2. Add two cups water, tomatoes, tomato sauce, oregano, cumin, chili powder, lemon juice, cayenne pepper, and black pepper. Cook uncovered over low heat for 15 minutes.

3. Sprinkle each serving with 1 tsp. grated Cheddar or Parmesan cheese (if desired) before serving. Makes eight portions.

Per serving:

Calories:	280	**Carb.:**	50 g.
Fat:	3 g.	**Sodium:**	488 mg.
Protein:	16 g.		

RECIPES (cont.)

APPLE RAISIN PANCAKES

Ingredients:

2 cups all-purpose flour
2 tbsp. sugar
1 tbsp. low-sodium baking powder
2 tsp. ground cinnamon
1-3/4 cups skim milk
1/2 cup Egg-Beaters®*
1/4 cup unsalted margarine, melted
3/4 cup chopped apple
3/4 cup seedless raisins

*Cholesterol-free egg product

Directions:

1. In medium bowl, combine flour, sugar, baking powder, and cinnamon.

2. In small bowl, beat together skim milk, Egg Beaters® and margarine; stir into dry ingredients. Mix in apples and raisins.
3. Using 1/4 cup batter for each pancake, cook on lightly greased nonstick skillet or griddle over medium-high heat, turning once to brown on both sides. Makes 14 pancakes.

Per serving:

Calories:	147	**Sodium:**	37 mg.
Fat:	3 g.	**Saturated fatty acids:**	0 g.
Cholesterol:	1 mg.		

SAMPLE PREGNANCY MENU

Breakfast
1/2 banana
1 cup iron-fortified cereal
1 slice whole-wheat toast
1 tsp. margarine
1 cup 2% milk

Food Group
fruit
bread
bread
fat
dairy

Mid-morning snack:
3 graham crackers
1/2 cup apple juice

bread
fruit

Lunch
1 cup vegetable soup
2 oz. turkey
2 slices whole-wheat bread
lettuce and tomato
carrot and celery sticks
1 apple
1 cup 2% milk

Food Group
vegetable
protein
bread
vegetable
vegetable
fruit
dairy

Mid-afternoon snack:
1 slice whole-wheat toast
1 tbsp. peanut butter
1/2 cup orange juice

bread
protein
fruit

Dinner
3 oz. meat loaf
1 baked potato
1/2 cup spinach
1 dinner roll
1 tsp. margarine
1/2 cup mixed fruit
1 cup 2% milk

Food Group
protein
bread
vegetable
bread
fat
fruit
dairy

Evening snack:
1 cup yogurt

dairy

Go to www.ariselife-skills.org for fresh, vital lessons that connect youth emotionally and socially.

ARISE Foundation Order Toll-Free: 1-888-680-6100, Copyright © 1996-2009

SUBSTANCE ABUSE: ALCOHOL

Have a volunteer read the following out loud. Discuss your opinions on this subject.

Alcohol slows down the baby's oxygen flow, which he needs to grow. Drinking as little as one ounce of liquor while pregnant can cause lifelong physical problems and mental retardation for an unborn child.

Constant use of alcohol during pregnancy can lead to something called Fetal Alcohol Syndrome (FAS). FAS slows growth before and after birth. Defects in the limbs and heart, as well as deformed facial features, may result from the use of alcohol. The child may also have poor speech and coordination.

Danger: *Over-the-counter cough and cold remedies contain as much as 25 percent alcohol.*

Go to www.ariselife-skills.org for fresh, vital lessons that connect youth emotionally and socially.

SUBSTANCE ABUSE: CAFFEINE

Have another volunteer read this page. Did you know drinking a cup of coffee or soda could harm your baby? Discuss your thoughts on the topics.

Caffeine may be found in the following items:

- Coffee
- Carbonated beverages (sodas)
- Medication
- Tea
- Chocolate

Caffeine can cause the following birth defects:

- Smaller head size in newborns
- Low birth weight
- Premature labor
- Increased breathing problems for infants

ARISE Foundation, Order Toll-Free: 1-888-680-6100, Copyright © 1996-2009

SUBSTANCE ABUSE: CAFFEINE (cont.)

Draw a line to match the words on the left to the correct answer on the right.

1. Coffee

2. SIDS

3. Low birth weight

4. Soft drinks

5. Tea

6. Caffeine

7. Chocolate

a. Sudden Infant Death Syndrome

b. Ingredient found in ice cream, candy, and cookies

c. Many medications (especially those that prevent you from falling asleep) contain high amounts of this

d. Drink (usually with breakfast)

e. Can occur in babies as a result of too much caffeine

f. Popular beverages that contain carbonation

g. A refreshing drink that can be served warm or cold

Go to www.ariselife-skills.org for fresh, vital lessons that connect youth emotionally and socially.

SUBSTANCE ABUSE: CIGARETTES

Have a volunteer read this page to the group.

If a woman smokes cigarettes during pregnancy, her blood vessels tighten and reduce the amount of food and oxygen reaching her baby. Children who grow up around smokers have more bronchitis (constant swelling of the bronchial tubes), pneumonia, and respiratory infections. (The amount of infection depends on the amount of smoke in the home.) The greatest damage from breathing in someone else's cigarette smoke happens to infants under two years of age.

Smoking does the following:
- increases the risk of fetal damage
- heightens risk of pulmonary lung disease
- may result in low intelligence for your baby
- causes a higher rate of chronic bronchitis and emphysema
- may result in difficulties during pregnancy, including miscarriage, spontaneous abortion, and premature, low-birth-weight infants
- causes cancer
- increases risk of Sudden Infant Death Syndrome (SIDS)

Something to think about: There's a reason why this label appears on cigarettes.

SURGEON GENERAL'S WARNING: Smoking by pregnant women may result in fetal injury, premature birth, and low birth weight.

Go to www.ariselife-skills.org for fresh, vital lessons that connect youth emotionally and socially.

ARISE Foundation Order Toll-Free: 1-888-680-6100, Copyright © 1996-2009

SUBSTANCE ABUSE: CIGARETTES (cont.)

When you stop smoking, your body responds rapidly to the following changes: Within...

20 minutes:	Your blood pressure, heart rate, and temperature of your hands and feet return to normal.
8 hours:	Oxygen and carbon dioxide levels in your blood return to normal.
1 day:	Likelihood of having a heart attack decreases.
2 days:	Your senses of smell and taste improve; nerve endings start to regrow.
2 weeks to 3 months:	Circulation becomes better and breathing improves; it becomes easier to walk.
1 to 9 months:	Decreased coughing, sinus congestion, shortness of breath, and fatigue.
1 year:	Happy birthday! Your excess risk of heart disease is now less than half of what it was a year ago.
5 years:	Risk of cancer of the lungs, mouth, throat, and esophagus is half that of a pack-a-day smoker.
10 years:	Danger of dying of lung cancer is similar to nonsmokers.
15 years:	Your risk is no greater for heart disease than if you never smoked.

Go to www.ariselife-skills.org for fresh, vital lessons that connect youth emotionally and socially.

SUBSTANCE ABUSE: DRUGS

Every known drug, including heroin, methadone, crack, "ice," LSD, PCP, and prescription drugs, causes serious harm to a developing fetus.

Side effects from drug use include:
- Long-term intellectual deficiencies and physical defects, such as missing fingers
- Stroke
- Smaller body size
- Poorly developed kidneys and intestines
- Low birth weight and stillbirth
- Higher rate of Sudden Infant Death Syndrome (SIDS)
- Complications during birth and delivery
- Malnutrition

ARISE Foundation, Order Toll-Free: 1-888-680-6100, Copyright © 1996-2009

Substance Abuse: Drugs (cont.)

Use the word bank below to find names of some dangerous drugs in the puzzle below. Answers may be vertical, horizontal, diagonal, or backward.

```
M   A   R   I   J   U   A   N   A   L
L   J   K   M   W   I   P   C   P   X
S   A   Q   P   I   N   O   V   H   U
C   C   A   C   I   C   Y   I   C   E
C   R   I   L   A   S   P   E   E   D
U   R   A   I   W   E   O   L   L   V
J   U   N   C   U   T   C   Z   S   P
Y   E   J   Y   K   N   M   I   D   M
E   L   N   I   O   R   E   H   U   W
```

WORD BANK

heroin	cocaine
marijuana	PCP
LSD	crack
ice	speed

Go to www.ariselife-skills.org for fresh, vital lessons that connect youth emotionally and socially.

SUBSTANCE ABUSE POSTER

Design a poster showing the effects of drugs, alcohol, and smoking on unborn children. Not all of us are born great artists. Do the best you can to satisfy yourself.

ARISE Foundation Order Toll-Free: 1-888-680-6100, Copyright © 1996-2009

A CARING PREGNANCY

List 10 ways for a woman to take care of herself during pregnancy. For these purposes, don't worry about grammar or spelling. Just do the best you can. The main idea is for you to participate

1. _____

2. _____

3. _____

4. _____

5. _____

6. _____

7. _____

8. _____

9. _____

   _____

10. _____

   _____

Go to www.ariselife-skills.org for fresh, vital lessons that connect youth emotionally and socially.

SIGNS OF TROUBLE

Gestational Diabetes

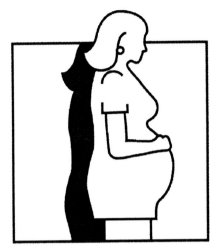

Bleeding

Contact your doctor immediately if the bleeding is heavy; the same day if it is light or spotty. Blood may signal a problem with the placenta or premature labor.

Signs may include unusual thirst, frequent and heavy urination, and fatigue. At 24 to 28 weeks into the pregnancy, most doctors test for gestational diabetes.

High Blood Pressure

Signs may include swelling of the hands and face and sudden weight gain due to water retention. This condition can quickly become serious. Signs include blurred vision, headaches, decreased urination, and severe stomach pain.

ARISE Foundation, Order Toll-Free: 1-888-680-6100, Copyright © 1996-2009

GESTATIONAL DIABETES

Things to Remember:

 Reduce your intake of foods high in sugar (syrups, honey, candy, sodas, desserts, fruit juices, and punch). Artificial sweeteners containing saccharin should also be avoided or used in very small amounts during pregnancy.

Eat consistently every day. Do not skip breakfast, lunch, or dinner. Have meals of similar size at the same time each day. This is especially important if taking insulin. Don't allow more than six hours to pass between meals.

 Watch the number of calories you take in! This is not the time to lose lots of weight — or gain plenty of it — either. Most women with gestational diabetes need to eat between 1,800 and 2,200 calories per day.

Get regular moderate exercise. A daily walk that lasts 30 to 40 minutes is a good activity for a pregnant woman.

Take in three balanced meals. Choose from the different food groups and have one to three snacks per day.

Go to www.ariselife-skills.org for fresh, vital lessons that connect youth emotionally and socially.

GESTATIONAL DIABETES (cont.)

Have three to four eight-ounce servings of
milk or low-fat yogurt daily as meals or snacks.
Do not use sweetened or regular frozen yogurt.

Choose low-fat foods.

You may have one serving of fruit with
breakfast, lunch, and dinner.

Avoid sugar.

Don't eat too much food containing caffeine.

Don't drink alcohol.

Don't take drugs.

Don't smoke.

Test your blood glucose regularly according
to the schedule provided by your doctor.

ARISE Foundation, Order Toll-Free: 1-888-680-6100, Copyright © 1996-2009

FOODS TO AVOID
CROSSWORD PUZZLE

Use the clues and word bank below to solve the crossword puzzle.

ACROSS

1. _____, such as potato chips, are very fattening and greasy. (two words)
5. Chocolate chip _____ are not a healthy snack for pregnant women.
6. _____ often come packaged in loads of sugary syrup. (two words)
7. Instead of putting _____ on a slice of toast, try sugar-free jelly.
8. Potato _____ are very salty and unhealthy.

DOWN

2. _____ is usually made with lots of sugar and whole milk. (two words)
3. Avoid drinking _____ during breakfast. (two words)
4. _____ is found in cookies, candies, and other sweets.

Word Bank		
fruit juice	canned fruits	chips
ice cream	cookies	fried foods
butter	sugar	

Go to www.ariselife-skills.org for fresh, vital lessons that connect youth emotionally and socially.

FOODS TO AVOID
CROSSWORD PUZZLE (cont.)

ARISE Foundation, Order Toll-Free: 1-888-680-6100, Copyright © 1996-2009

FOOD GUIDE: RECOMMENDED FOODS

Food Group	Number of Servings	Food Items
Breads and cereals	6 to 11	Brown rice, pasta, potatoes with skin, barley, oatmeal, shredded wheat
Fruits	2 to 3	Apples, pears, plums, peaches, bananas, grapefruits, oranges
Vegetables	4 to 8	Onions, scallions, carrots, celery, lettuce, broccoli, kale, cabbage, collards, spinach, okra, cucumbers, peppers, eggplants, mushrooms
Milk	3 to 4	Skim or 1% low-fat milk, low-fat yogurt, low-fat cheese
Meats and proteins	2 to 3 (3-oz. portion each)	Lean sirloin, lean chuck steak lean hamburger, skinless chicken and turkey, fish, beans, tofu, fat-free hot dogs, turkey franks, soy burgers
Fats	2 (1 tsp. per serving)	Diet margarine and butter, low-fat salad dressing, low-fat cream cheese, avocado, olive, peanut and corn oils
Beverages	1 cup per serving 8 glasses of water	Water, decaffeinated herb tea and coffee, seltzer water

Go to www.ariselife-skills.org for fresh, vital lessons that connect youth emotionally and socially.

Food Guide:
Matching Foods

Draw a line from the word(s) on the left to the correct answer on the right.

1. Breads and cereals

2. Vegetables

3. Fruits

4. Fats

5. Meats and proteins

6. Milk

7. Beverages

A. Turkey franks

B. Olive oil

C. Low-fat cheese

D. Pasta

E. Water

F. Orange

G. Broccoli

DIABETES MENU

Breakfast: 1 slice toast
1 oz. low-fat cheese
1 cup 1% milk

Mid-morning snack: 2 slices whole-wheat bread
2 tbsp. peanut butter
water or noncaloric beverage

Lunch: 2 slices whole-wheat bread
2 oz. lean ham
1 cup spinach salad
1 tsp. salad dressing
1 orange
1 cup 1% milk

Mid-afternoon snack: 1 cup low-fat yogurt with artificial
sweetener
3 graham crackers

Dinner: 2 oz. baked chicken
1 cup broccoli
1/2 cup rice
1 dinner roll
1 tsp. margarine
gelatin with artificial sweetener and 1/2 fruit
water or noncaloric beverage

Bedtime snack: 10 to 12 soda crackers
1/4 cup cottage cheese or 1 oz. low-fat cheese

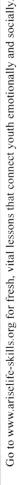

Go to www.ariselife-skills.org for fresh, vital lessons that connect youth emotionally and socially.

DIABETES DANGERS

Stillbirth

Overweight baby

Low blood glucose (hypoglycemia)
may develop in the baby
after delivery

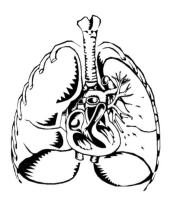

Respiratory distress
(difficulty breathing)

Presence of bilirubin (liver pigment)
which may cause the
baby's skin to look yellow

ARISE Foundation Order Toll-Free: 1-888-680-6100, Copyright © 1996–2009

LETTER TO MY FUTURE CHILD

Write a letter to your future child on how you plan to be a good parent. Express your fears, excitement, and plans for providing him with the best life possible. For these purposes, don't worry about grammar or spelling. Just do the best you can. The main idea is for you to participate.

Dear Child,

_____

_____

_____

_____

_____

_____

_____

_____

Your loving parent,

_____

Go to www.ariselife-skills.org for fresh, vital lessons that connect youth emotionally and socially.

KEY TIPS

Read the following and talk about your opinions:

1. A woman must see her doctor as soon as she thinks she may be pregnant.

2. The goal of prenatal care is the birth of a healthy baby to a healthy mother.

3. Good nutrition is necessary for development of a strong infant.

4. Eating foods low in nutrition and abusing alcohol and drugs lead to birth defects.

5. Women with gestational diabetes must take special care of themselves to avoid risking their lives and the future of their unborn children.

ARISE Foundation, Order Toll-Free: 1-888-680-6100, Copyright © 1996-2009

CHAPTER 1 QUIZ: PRENATAL CARE

Name: _____   Date: _____

Circle the correct answer for each statement.

1.   The following are signs of pregnancy:
    a.   nausea   b.   dizziness
    c.   vomiting   d.   all of the above

2.   Pregnant women should *not* eat too much of:
    a.   vegetables   b.   salty foods
    c.   fruits   d.   breads and cereals

3.   Two sexually transmitted diseases (STDs) are:
    a.   herpes and the flu   b.   syphilis and diabetes
    c.   herpes and syphilis   d.   none of the above

4.   Gestational diabetes:
    a.   can be controlled by diet   b.   can be deadly
    c.   is a sexually transmitted disease   d.   both a and b are correct

5.   Prenatal care:
    a.   will lead to a painless delivery   b.   can help find signs of possible problems
    c.   is very painful   d.   all of the above

Go to www.ariselife-skills.org for fresh, vital lessons that connect youth emotionally and socially.

DELIVERY VOCABULARY LIST

Amniotic fluid: Fluid that surrounds the baby in the uterus.

Anesthetic: Medication that provides relief from pain. One of the most common labor anesthetics is the epidural, which is inserted into a woman's lower spine to numb the lower half of her body. Epidurals are usually given during active labor.

Anterior position: Position of baby in uterus when back of head is toward mother's front.

APGAR score: A general test of the infant's well-being, given immediately after birth to measure heart, breathing, circulation, and nerve response.

Braxton-Hicks contractions: Contractions of uterus that happen throughout pregnancy, but may not be noticed until the ninth month.

Breech presentation: Position of baby who is bottom or feet down rather than head down in the uterus.

Cervix: Lower entrance to uterus.

Circumcision: Operation to remove foreskin from a male infant's penis. It's mostly performed without anesthetic and may be quite painful for the child.

Contraction: Tightening of the uterine muscles during labor to press baby down through the birth canal.

Crowning: When largest part of child's head appears in vagina and does not slip back again.

Dilation: Progressive opening of cervix caused by contractions of uterus during labor. Average final dilation size is 10 centimeters.

Effacement: Cervix becomes thinner, shorter, and softer in preparation for birth.

Episiotomy: Surgical cut in perineum to enlarge vagina in order to allow infant's passage.

Fallopian tube: Tube through which a ripe egg travels to the uterus after leaving the ovary.

DELIVERY VOCABULARY LIST (cont.)

Fetal distress: Shortage in oxygen flow to the baby; this can be due to numerous causes.

Hemorrhoids: Swelling of blood vessels in rectum.

Hormones: Chemical messenger produced by an organ that regulates activities of a specific organ.

Hypertension: High blood pressure; it can be brought on by pregnancy.

Induced labor: Method of artificially causing labor to start.

Lamaze method: Way of childbirth where mothers and their partners are taught how to use relaxation, breathing techniques, and exercises to prepare for delivery.

Non-stress test: Fetal monitor that evaluates fetal condition in uterus and condition of the placenta. A reactive NST indicates a healthy baby.

Perineum: Area located between vulva and anus in the female. It also includes muscles and tissues of lower pelvic area.

Placenta: Part of uterus that gives baby nourishment, also called the "afterbirth."

Postpartum: Time following the birth.

Presentation: How the infant is positioned for birth: head, buttocks, feet. Part closest to cervical opening is called the "presenting part."

Transition phase: End of first stage of labor. Contractions are very strong. This is the most difficult time to deal with.

Uterus: Organ in which fetus develops. It is also called the womb.

Go to www.ariselife-skills.org for fresh, vital lessons that connect youth emotionally and socially.

DELIVERY DEFINITIONS

Match words on left with definitions on right by placing the correct letter in space provided.

1. _____ Anterior position

A. A shortage in the flow of oxygen to the baby; can be due to numerous causes.

2. _____ Braxton-Hicks contractions

B. Position of the infant in uterus when back of the head is toward the mother's front.

3. _____ Breech presentation

C. Operation to cut foreskin from the penis, usually performed soon after delivery.

4. _____ Circumcision

D. Contractions of the uterus that happen throughout pregnancy, but which may not be noticed until the ninth month.

5. _____ Fetal distress

E. Position of baby, who is bottom or feet down.

6. _____ Non-stress test

F. End of first stage of labor. Contractions are very strong. This is the most difficult time to cope with.

7. _____ Perineum

G. Electronic fetal monitor that evaluates fetal condition in the uterus and the condition of the placenta.

8. _____ Transition phase

H. Area located between vulva and anus in the female. It also includes muscles and tissues of the lower pelvic area.

ARISE Foundation Order Toll-Free: 1-888-680-6100, Copyright © 1996-2009

PREGNANCY WORD SEARCH

Use the word bank to answer clues at the bottom of the page. Next, locate the words in the puzzle.

A	N	E	S	T	H	E	T	I	C	M
S	T	I	D	E	A	T	H	S	E	D
C	B	G	P	X	D	O	J	J	R	I
C	R	O	W	N	I	N	G	G	V	L
U	T	E	R	U	S	A	D	E	I	A
A	N	I	E	G	G	E	V	O	X	T
R	L	N	I	C	E	J	N	S	E	I
K	K	G	I	R	L	S	B	T	G	O
C	O	N	T	R	A	C	T	I	O	N

1. An _____ is given to reduce pain.
2. _____ is the opening of the cervix during labor.
3. The lower entrance to the uterus is called the _____.
4. _____ is another name for the womb.
5. A _____ is the tightening of the uterine muscles during labor.
6. _____ is when the baby's head appears in the vagina.

WORD BANK

crowning	anesthetic	contraction
dilation	cervix	uterus

Go to www.ariselife-skills.org for fresh, vital lessons that connect youth emotionally and socially.

SCRAMBLED DELIVERY

Refer to words on the vocabulary list to solve and unscramble those in the sentences below.

1. FANTCEEEFM is the thinning out of the cervix.

    _____

2. Fluid surrounding the baby in the uterus is called the NIOAICMT FDLIU.

    _____

3. AAGPR OERSC is a general test of the infant's well-being.

    _____

4. The time following birth is called PAUMRTOSTP.

    _____

5. ERRHHOIMODS are swelling of the blood vessels in the rectum.

    _____

6. ECTANPLA is the part of the uterus that nourishes baby.

    _____

7. An PMSIOITOEY is a surgical cut to enlarge the vagina.

    _____

8. How the child is positioned for birth is called SENTTIARONPE.

    _____

9. NESRMHOO are chemical messengers produced by organs.

    _____

10. UCEINDD OLABR is a method of stimulating labor.

    _____

Delivery, Postpartum, and Infant Needs

Delivery

1. Watch with a second hand to time contractions
2. Lotion or powder for massages
3. Heavy socks to wear if your feet get cold
4. Tennis ball for massage
5. Lollipops to keep mouth moist
6. Camera and film
7. Breath spray

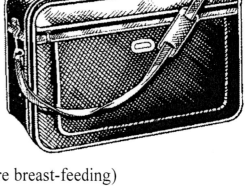

For the Mother — Postpartum

1. Loose clothes to wear home
2. Four pairs of panties
3. One or two nightgowns (with front opening if you are breast-feeding)
4. Robe and slippers
5. Nursing bras if you are breast-feeding, regular bras if not
6. Insurance information
7. Sanitary pads
8. Hairbrush
9. Toothbrush and toothpaste
10. Shampoo
11. Deodorant
12. Lip balm
13. Eyeglasses or contact lenses
14. Soap
15. Perfume
16. Pillow

For the Newborn at the Hospital

1. Disposable diapers
2. 2 to 3 gowns
3. 2 to 3 pairs of booties or socks
4. 1 to 2 receiving blankets
5. 2 to 3 undershirts
6. Clothes to wear home

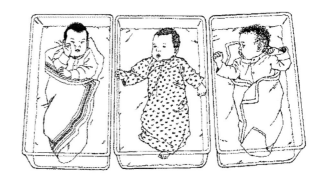

Go to www.ariselife-skills.org for fresh, vital lessons that connect youth emotionally and socially.

DELIVERY, POSTPARTUM, AND INFANT NEEDS (cont.)

FOR THE NEWBORN AT HOME

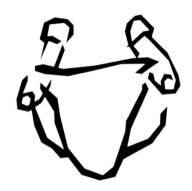

CLOTHING
1. Nightgowns
2. Stretch suits
3. Shirts
4. Sweaters
5. Waterproof pants
6. Warm sleepers

BATHING AND CLEANSING
1. Baby bathtub
2. Soft towels and washcloths
3. Cotton balls
4. Diaper rash ointment
5. Baby shampoo
6. Petroleum jelly (Vaseline)
7. Baby nail scissors (blunt tips)
8. Cloth diapers and diaper pins or disposable diapers
9. Diaper pail (especially for cloth diapers)

BEDDING
1. Waterproof pads
2. Fitted crib sheets
3. Soft baby blankets

MISCELLANEOUS
1. Cold water vaporizer
2. Baby monitor

FOR SITTING, CARRYING, AND TRAVELING
1. Front (sling-type) carrier
2. Infant seat
3. Car seat
4. Stroller
5. Diaper bag

DELIVERY, POSTPARTUM, AND INFANT NEEDS (cont.)

Place items from the list below in the correct column.

Things I need to take to hospital:

_____ _____
_____ _____
_____ _____
_____ _____
_____ _____
_____ _____
_____ _____
_____ _____
_____ _____
_____ _____
_____ _____
_____ _____

Things I need to have at home:

_____ _____
_____ _____
_____ _____
_____ _____
_____ _____
_____ _____
_____ _____
_____ _____
_____ _____
_____ _____
_____ _____

lotion or powder
tennis ball for massage
sweaters
waterproof pants
warm sleepers
baby bathtub
soft towels and washcloths
cotton balls
diaper rash ointment
lollipops
camera and film
breath spray
loose maternity clothes
four pairs of panties
robe and slippers
nursing bras
insurance information

sanitary pads
hairbrush
toothbrush and toothpaste
shampoo, soap
deodorant
lip balm
eyeglasses and contact lenses
disposable diapers
2 to 3 gowns
2 to 3 pairs of booties or socks
1 to 2 receiving blankets
2 to 3 undershirts
clothes to wear home
nightgowns
stretch suits
shirts
baby shampoo

petroleum jelly
baby nail scissors
diaper pail
waterproof pads
fitted crib sheets
soft baby blankets
cold water vaporizer
baby monitor
front (sling-type) carrier
infant seat
car seat
stroller
diaper bag
watch with a second hand
heavy socks
nightgowns

IMAGINE YOUR DELIVERY

Write a story about what you picture will happen on your future delivery day. For these purposes, don't worry about grammar or spelling. Just do the best you can. The main idea is for you to participate.

_____

_____

_____

_____

_____

_____

_____

_____

ARISE Foundation, Order Toll-Free: 1-888-680-6100, Copyright © 1996-2009

EMERGENCY CONTACT CARD

Complete the information and keep this sheet for easy reference.

Emergency: **911**

Doctor's Name: _____

Doctor's Telephone
Number: _____

FAMILY MEMBERS

Name   Telephone Number

_____   _____

_____   _____

_____   _____

In case of a 911 call, give this information:

Your Name: _____

Telephone
Number: _____

Address: _____

Due Date: _____

Go to www.ariselife-skills.org for fresh, vital lessons that connect youth emotionally and socially.

MY PERFECT BABY SHOWER

In the space below, write some plans for your ideal baby shower. Include games to play, decorations, and food. Next, list gifts you'd like to receive and then make a list of people to invite.

Activities we can do at the shower:

_____   _____

_____   _____

_____   _____

_____   _____

My gift wish list:

_____   _____

_____   _____

_____   _____

_____   _____

People to invite:

_____   _____

_____   _____

_____   _____

_____   _____

ARISE Foundation, Order Toll-Free: 1-888-680-6100, Copyright © 1996-2009

AM I IN LABOR?

Read each symptom and place it in either the "true labor" or "false labor" category.

<table>
<tr><td align="center">TRUE LABOR</td><td align="center">FALSE LABOR</td></tr>
<tr><td>_____</td><td>_____</td></tr>
<tr><td>_____</td><td>_____</td></tr>
<tr><td>_____</td><td>_____</td></tr>
<tr><td>_____</td><td>_____</td></tr>
<tr><td>_____</td><td>_____</td></tr>
<tr><td>_____</td><td>_____</td></tr>
</table>

Contractions...

feel the same on either side, beginning at cervix and moving up and around to the back, or beginning at the lower back and moving to the front.

are not affected by drinking a glass of water.

begin in front but may not move to the back.

may become longer or stronger.

occur in a regular pattern.

grow longer, stronger, and occur closer together.

don't follow a regular pattern in most cases.

stop if a woman changes her activity.

stop when a woman drinks water.

do not stop if a woman changes her activity.

Go to www.ariselife-skills.org for fresh, vital lessons that connect youth emotionally and socially.

COMMON DELIVERY PROCEDURES

Perineal shaving: A complete perineal "prep" involves shaving all the hair from the pubic and perineal areas. A partial prep involves shaving only hair on the perineum. Often no shaving is performed.

Enema: An enema is a liquid put in the rectum to empty bowels and allow more room in the birth canal or to help speed labor by stimulating contractions. This procedure isn't always done.

Intravenous line (IV): An IV may be inserted into a vein in the mother's arm or hand and can be used to give medication when necessary. IVs also provide fluids and calories during labor.

Artificial rupture of the membrane: Breaking the bag of water is sometimes done routinely in early labor. Without artificial rupture, it usually does not break until late in the first or second stage of labor.

Electronic fetal monitoring (EFM): EFM gives a record of fetal heart rate. The device may be attached to mother's abdomen or internally to an infant's scalp.

Episiotomy: An episiotomy is a cut into the perineum to enlarge the vaginal opening.

Cesarean section: A C-section is a surgical procedure to remove a baby from the mother's uterus. Today, about one in four American infants are born by this method. This may be planned or done in an emergency situation. Pregnant women must discuss with their doctors whether they will give birth naturally or have a C-section.

Some examples of when a C-section may be necessary include:

- When the umbilical cord emerges from birth canal before baby
- Fetal distress
- Breech presentation (baby is upside down in uterus)
- Multiple pregnancy
- When the infant's head is too large to fit through birth canal
- Labor slows down or stops
- Active herpes lesions exist
- Child is overdue

ORDER OF DELIVERY

Read the steps below and place them in correct order from one to eight (one being what will happen first).

_____   A nurse may give the baby an APGAR test.

_____   The labor room attendant will wipe off baby and clear airways.

_____   Infant will be placed on the mother's abdomen to be held, admired, and cuddled.

_____   The baby's head will emerge and a nurse will suction his nose and mouth.

_____   After the first round of testing, a doctor cuts the umbilical cord. Infant is moved to another table, rubbed down with a towel, weighed, footprinted, given an ID bracelet, and wrapped in a blanket. Eye drops are usually given to prevent infection.

_____   The mother is cleaned and stitched (if an episiotomy was performed).

_____   The placenta is withdrawn, uterine cavity is examined and cleaned.

_____   The baby is returned to his mother's arms.

Go to www.ariselife-skills.org for fresh, vital lessons that connect youth emotionally and socially.

KEY TIPS

Read the following and talk about your thoughts about these statements:

1. Expectant mothers must prepare for delivery by organizing materials needed at home and hospital for themselves and their babies.

2. Delivery and birth are easier to manage when parents make arrangements with the hospital, babysitters, and family members ahead of time.

3. It's very important to keep an emergency contact card where it can be easily seen.
    It could save a life!

ARISE Foundation, Order Toll-Free: 1-888-680-6100, Copyright © 1996-2009

Chapter 2 Quiz: Delivery

Name: _____   Date: _____

Circle the correct answer for each statement.

1. It's a good idea for pregnant women to:
   a. tour the hospital where they'll be having the baby
   b. ask their doctors many questions
   c. prepare an emergency contact card
   d. all of the above

2. A woman may feel contractions:
   a. only during the last month of pregnancy
   b. only in the first month of pregnancy
   c. throughout pregnancy
   d. none of the above

3. "Hypertension" is another word for:
   a. stress
   b. high blood pressure
   c. contractions
   d. none of the above

4. An emergency contact card must list:
   a. the doctor's name and phone number
   b. family members' telephone numbers
   c. the police and fire emergency number
   d. all of the above

5. During "true" labor:
   a. contractions grow longer and stronger
   b. drinking water will relieve contractions
   c. contractions do not stop if a woman changes her activity
   d. both a and c are correct

Go to www.ariselife-skills.org for fresh, vital lessons that connect youth emotionally and socially.

CHANGES IN MY LIFE

Write about the changes you think will happen in your life when you bring home a new baby. For these purposes, don't worry about grammar or spelling. Just do the best you can. The main idea is for you to participate.

_____

_____

_____

_____

_____

_____

_____

_____

_____

_____

_____

Go to www.ariselife-skills.org for fresh, vital lessons that connect youth emotionally and socially.

ARISE Foundation Order Toll-Free: 1-888-680-6100, Copyright © 1996-2009

POSTPARTUM MISCONCEPTIONS

Read each of the statements below. If you think the statement is true, write a "T" in the space; if it is false, write an "F."

_____ After an infant is cleaned up, he will be beautiful and look like the picture on a baby-food jar.

_____ After giving birth, a woman quickly loses all of the weight she gained during pregnancy.

_____ New mothers are so happy with their new children that nothing else matters.

_____ New mothers will be in some pain for a while and need help with things such as housework and baby care.

_____ Since breast-feeding is natural, it is easy to do.

_____ If a woman bleeds after giving birth and returning home, she should call a doctor immediately.

_____ Only rotten parents get frustrated with their new baby.

Go to www.ariselife-skills.org for fresh, vital lessons that connect youth emotionally and socially.

POSTPARTUM SYMPTOMS

During the first six postpartum weeks, post-childbirth difficulties may occur. Some of these problems include:

Bleeding that soaks more than one pad per hour for more than a few hours. A woman must go to the emergency room if she is unable to immediately contact her doctor.

Persistent bright red bleeding any time after the fourth postpartum day.

More than one large (lemon size or larger) blood clot.

No bleeding at all during first two weeks.

Pain or discomfort in lower abdominal area (stomach).

After first 24 hours, a temperature of greater than 100 degrees for more than one day.

Sharp chest pain. Women should go to the emergency room if they are unable to immediately contact their doctor.

Localized pain, tenderness, and warmth in the calf; swelling and pain when flexing feet.

A lump or hardened area in breast.

Localized pain, swelling, redness, heat, and tenderness in breast.

Localized swelling, redness, heat, or oozing at the site of a cesarean incision.

Difficulty urinating; pain or burning upon urination.

Depression which affects a woman's ability to cope and doesn't stop after a few days.

Feelings of anger toward the baby, especially if these feelings occur with violent urges.

If a new mother experiences any of these problems,
she must call her doctor immediately!

ARISE Foundation, Order Toll-Free: 1-888-680-6100, Copyright © 1996-2009

POSTPARTUM SYMPTOMS (cont.)

Read each symptom below and decide if it requires a phone call to the doctor.

YES	NO	
❏	❏	Bleeding that soaks more than one pad per hour for more than a few hours.
❏	❏	No bleeding at all during the first two weeks.
❏	❏	Low temperature for about three hours.
❏	❏	Localized swelling, redness, heat, or oozing at the site of a cesarean incision.
❏	❏	Pain in perineal area.
❏	❏	Feelings of sadness and unhappiness continuing for more than one day.
❏	❏	Sharp chest pain.
❏	❏	Feelings of anger toward baby, particularly if these are accompanied by violent urges.
❏	❏	A lump or hardened area in breast.
❏	❏	Sore and cracked nipples.

Go to www.ariselife-skills.org for fresh, vital lessons that connect youth emotionally and socially.

New Parent Survival Tips

Avoid becoming overtired.

Make an effort to rest.

Stay in bed and take it easy.

Wear a comfortable robe or loose clothes.

Take naps. Sleep when baby naps.

Go to bed early.

Don't start new projects.

Take time for yourself.

Spend time as a couple.

Request guests make their visits short.

Avoid hosting parties or get-togethers.

Get help and support from family and friends.

Ask for help with shopping and errands.

Get someone to assist with laundry.

Seek help cooking meals and cleaning up.

Eat a balanced diet.

Drink plenty of water (six to eight glasses per day).

Avoid alcohol and drugs.

Go to www.ariselife-skills.org for fresh, vital lessons that connect youth emotionally and socially.

ARISE Foundation, Order Toll-Free: 1-888-680-6100, Copyright © 1996-2009

NEW PARENT STRESS MANAGEMENT

Make a list of trusted family members, friends, and acquaintances whom you feel comfortable asking for help. Using the key at the bottom of the page, write the kinds of support you can expect next to each person's name. The first one has been done for you. Keep in mind one person can give you different kinds of support. For these purposes, don't worry about grammar or spelling. Just do the best you can. The main idea is for you to participate.

1. *Linda Ruiz* — **E** _____

2. _____

3. _____

4. _____

5. _____

6. _____

7. _____

8. _____

E: emotional
F: financial
I: informational
P: physical
S: spiritual

12 Tips to Get a Grip

1. Take a deep breath. Remember: You are the adult.

2. Close your eyes. Imagine you hear what the child does or picture receiving the same punishment as you give the youngster.

3. Press lips together and count to 20.

4. Put the child in a "time-out" chair for a few minutes. (Suggestion: one minute of time out for each year of age.)

5. Put yourself in a "time-out" chair. Are you really angry at the youngster or is something else bothering you?

6. If someone can watch the child, go for a walk.

7. Take a hot bath or splash cold water on your face.

8. Hug a pillow.

9. Call a friend to talk about your anger. If necessary, call the National Child Hotline (1-800-4-A-CHILD).

10. Turn on some relaxing music.

11. Pick up a pencil and write a list of helpful words, not any that will hurt. Save this paper and use it.

12. Send for more information to help you keep calm. Write to:

Childhelp USA
6463 Independence Avenue
Woodland Hills, CA 91367

Go to www.ariselife-skills.org for fresh, vital lessons that connect youth emotionally and socially.

ARISE Foundation, Order Toll-Free: 1-888-680-6100, Copyright © 1996-2009

SUPPORT YOURSELF

Write a letter describing why you deserve support. Remember to use tips from the worksheet. A few sentences have been provided to get you started. For these purposes, don't worry about grammar or spelling. Just do the best you can. The main idea is for you to participate.

I am a worthy person who is going to devote time to nurturing and caring for this sweet baby. Because of this, I deserve help from other family members, particularly my _____.

_____

_____

_____

_____

_____

_____

_____

_____

_____

Go to www.ariselife-skills.org for fresh, vital lessons that connect youth emotionally and socially.

WHAT TO DO WITH ANGER

Place an "X" on the boxes describing good ways to deal with anger.

Count to 10.

Go for a
long walk.

Yell and scream.

Throw things
that will break.

Hit others.

Call a close friend
and complain.

Remove yourself
from the problem.

Curse.

Pray for
understanding.

Go to www.ariselife-skills.org for fresh, vital lessons that connect youth emotionally and socially.

ARISE Foundation, Order Toll-Free: 1-888-680-6100, Copyright © 1996-2009

A LETTER TO MY PARTNER

Write a letter to your future partner about what you expect from him before and after you have given birth. For these purposes, don't worry about grammar or spelling. Just do the best you can. The main idea is for you to participate.

Dear _____,

_____

_____

_____

_____

_____

_____

_____

_____

_____

_____

(Your signature)

SETTING GOALS

List below what you want to get done this week. Place the most important items in column A, the next under B, and the least important in the C column. For these purposes, don't worry about grammar or spelling. Just do the best you can. The main idea is for you to participate.

A	B	C

ARISE Foundation, Order Toll-Free: 1-888-680-6100, Copyright © 1996-2009

TIME MANAGEMENT

Think about important "must-do" items in your life. Assign them "A," "B," or "C," in order of importance. Set times and dates for completion. For these purposes, don't worry about grammar or spelling. Just do the best you can. The main idea is for you to participate.

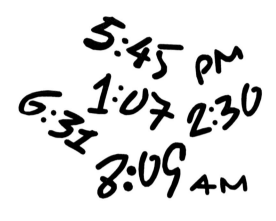

Job to be done	Date to be completed	Level of priority
_____	_____	_____
_____	_____	_____
_____	_____	_____
_____	_____	_____
_____	_____	_____
_____	_____	_____

Go to www.ariselife-skills.org for fresh, vital lessons that connect youth emotionally and socially.

ORGANIZING SPACE

An organized space makes caring for an infant much easier. Think about all of the things new parents need on or near a changing table. Make a list of these items. For these purposes, don't worry about grammar or spelling. Just do the best you can.

Products needed in changing area:

_____

_____

_____

_____

_____

_____

_____

ARISE Foundation, Order Toll-Free: 1-888-680-6100, Copyright © 1996-2009

BABY AT HOME
CROSSWORD PUZZLE

Use the clues and word bank below to solve the crossword puzzle.

ACROSS

5. New parents must learn to _____ time wisely.
7. Taking care of a new baby is easier when parents are
_____.

8. Items, such as diapers and baby powder, should be kept on or
near a changing _____.

DOWN

1. Caring for a baby will take up most of a parent's _____.
2. New mothers need _____ from their partners, family
members, and friends.
3. Even though breastfeeding is _____, it's not always
easy to do.
4. Expect many _____ in your life once you have a baby.
6. It will take some time for a new mom to lose the _____ she
gained during pregnancy.

Word Bank			
natural	support	manage	organized
weight	table	changes	time

Go to www.ariselife-skills.org for fresh, vital lessons that connect youth emotionally and socially.

KEY TIPS

Read the following out loud:

1. Expect many changes in your life when you have a baby.

2. Stress is the new parent's enemy; it's important to relax and learn how to pace yourself after having a baby.

3. Controlling anger and managing temper is a skill every parent must learn.

4. Seek support and help from your partner, family members, and friends once you have a child.

5. Learn to manage time well. It will help you greatly when juggling household responsibilities.

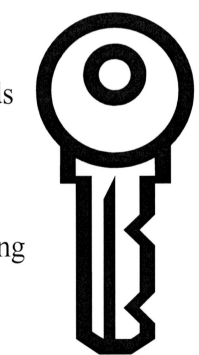

Go to www.ariselife-skills.org for fresh, vital lessons that connect youth emotionally and socially.

CHAPTER 3 QUIZ: POSTPARTUM EXPECTATIONS

Name: _____   Date: _____

Circle the correct answer for each statement.

1. The following is a false belief people have about babies:
    a. it costs a lot to care for a baby
    c. all babies are cute after they are born
    b. infants rarely sleep through the night
    d. all of the above

2. A woman may feel this symptom after having a baby:
    a. a lot of hunger
    c. exhaustion
    b. nausea
    d. none of the above

3. Breast-feeding:
    a. is a learned skill
    c. is always painful
    b. is natural
    d. both a and b are correct

4. To release anger and stress, parents can:
    a. take a walk
    c. yell at their child
    b. spank their baby
    d. both b and c are correct

5. Setting goals will help new parents:
    a. get organized
    c. make time to do all their chores
    b. avoid stress
    d. all of the above

TALK SHOW
ROLE CARD: HOST

"Good morning (afternoon). Welcome to our special segment on **Drugs and Smoking During Pregnancy.** We're here today to talk about the effects smoking and drugs may have on a pregnant mother and her unborn child."

"We have with us a distinguished panel of guests, including:

Dr. Kaplan, a local pediatrician;
Kathy Myers, a representative from the American Lung Association;
Julia, a mother-to-be who smokes two packs of cigarettes per day;
Marta, a recovering drug addict;
and **Mary**, a foster mother of a crack-addicted baby."

"Please welcome our panelists to the show."

"We're here today to discuss how dangerous drinking alcohol is to an unborn child. Drinking while pregnant can cause lifelong physical problems and is among the most common causes of preventable mental retardation in a baby."

"Smoking cigarettes also increases risk of fetal damage and may result in low intelligence for your baby. It may also cause difficulties during pregnancy, including miscarriage and spontaneous abortion, and is the most common cause of premature, low-birth-weight infants. Women who smoke have infants one-half lighter in weight than nonsmoking mothers. Smoking also increases the risk of Sudden Infant Death Syndrome (SIDS)."

"I'd like to begin by introducing Dr. Kaplan, a pediatrician who specializes in Fetal Alcohol Syndrome (FAS). Tell us, Dr. Kaplan, what exactly is FAS?"

(Dr. Kaplan responds)

"Next, we have Kathy Myers from the American Lung Association who will share with us some of the dangers of smoking both during and after pregnancy. Ms. Myers..."

(Ms. Myers speaks)

Go to www.ariselife-skills.org for fresh, vital lessons that connect youth emotionally and socially.

TALK SHOW (cont.)

(Once Ms. Myers has responded, ask if there are any questions from the audience. Select one or two volunteers who have their hands raised to ask questions of the panel.)

"Now, we have Julia, a mother-to-be who continues to smoke. Julia, tell us, even knowing the danger cigarette smoking poses, why do you continue?"

(Julia speaks)

"Fourth, welcome Marta, a recovering drug addict who is concerned her drug abuse may have a negative effect on her unborn child. Marta, share your story with us..."

(Marta responds)

"Our last panelist is Mary, a foster mother of a crack-addicted baby. She is here to tell us about her first-hand experience with a child whose mother abused drugs during her pregnancy."

(Mary speaks)

(Once Mary finishes, go through the audience and select those audience members with role cards to ask their questions. Allow enough time for the panel members to answer. If time permits, ask if there are any audience members with additional questions or concerns regarding smoking or drug use during pregnancy. Again, allow the panel members to answer.)

"Thank you very much for joining us today and remember: **Drugs, smoking, and pregnancy don't mix!"**

ARISE Foundation, Order Toll-Free: 1-888-680-6100, Copyright © 1996-2009

TALK SHOW (cont.)
ROLE CARD: DR. KAPLAN

You are a pediatrician who deals with children suffering from Fetal Alcohol Syndrome (FAS), a condition that develops in children of mothers who drink alcohol while pregnant. You want to let everyone know the dangers of doing this during pregnancy.

Point out the amount of alcohol that is harmful may be very little; this is why it should be avoided, even in over-the-counter medications such as cough drops (which contain alcohol). These must only be used with a doctor's advice.

You want to share the following side effects of Fetal Alcohol Syndrome with the audience. Most severe forms of FAS cause:

- small body size and weight
- deformed bones, facial features, and organs
- mental retardation

However, the above side effects only account for 10 percent of kids who've been exposed to alcohol. There may be a much larger group of children who have been affected to a lesser degree, but who would be better off if their mothers had not consumed alcohol during pregnancy.

Go to www.ariselife-skills.org for fresh, vital lessons that connect youth emotionally and socially.

TALK SHOW (cont.)
ROLE CARD: KATHY MYERS

You work for the American Lung Association and know about the dangers of smoking during pregnancy. You want everyone who is pregnant or trying to have a baby to stop smoking. You even have some ideas about how they can quit.

Share the following dangers of smoking during pregnancy:

- having a miscarriage or stillborn baby
- giving birth to a premature infant
- having a child with learning and/or behavioral problems
- having an infant who will die from Sudden Infant Death Syndrome (SIDS)
- having a child who grows up to become a smoker
- giving birth to a baby who is smaller than average due to exposure to the 1,800 different chemicals found in one cigarette

You also know that in addition to causing damage to the fetus, smoking harms children who breathe in second-hand smoke. Youngsters who live with smokers:

- get sick more often and stay ill for longer periods of time
- have more coughs, colds, ear infections, and asthma attacks
- are more likely to suffer from heart disease, breathing problems, or lung cancer when they grow up

You have worked with many patients over the years and developed the following method to help them quit smoking:

1. Write down why you want to stop.
2. Ask a friend or partner to help you.
3. Throw away all cigarettes.
4. Avoid places that make you want to smoke.
5. Consider using nicotine patches to break your addiction.

Go to www.ariselife-skills.org for fresh, vital lessons that connect youth emotionally and socially.

ARISE Foundation Order Toll-Free: 1-888-680-6100. Copyright © 1996-2009

TALK SHOW (cont.)
ROLE CARD: JULIA

You are a 19-year-old woman who is five months pregnant. You have been smoking since you were 14 years old. You know smoking is dangerous for both you and your unborn baby and have tried to quit a number of times, but have been unsuccessful.

Go to www.ariselife-skills.org for fresh, vital lessons that connect youth emotionally and socially.

TALK SHOW (cont.)
ROLE CARD: MARTA

You are an 18-year-old female who is having unprotected sex on a regular basis. You have had a baby, but put him up for adoption.

You are also a recovering crack-cocaine addict. You think you might be pregnant again and are nervous your drug use may affect your unborn child.

ARISE Foundation, Order Toll-Free: 1-888-680-6100, Copyright © 1996-2009

TALK SHOW (cont.)
ROLE CARD: MARY

You are the foster mother of a three-year-old boy. Your son, Mark, was born to a crack-addicted mother and was also hooked when he was born. As an infant, your son would cry uncontrollably and have shaking fits. As he grew older, he was more hyper and aggressive than other children his age. You are now having him tested for learning disabilities because he has a hard time sitting still and paying attention.

TALK SHOW (cont.)
AUDIENCE CARDS

Is any amount of alcohol safe to drink while pregnant?

Even if an expectant mother doesn't smoke, is it dangerous for her to be around other people who light up?

Do drugs you took several years ago still threaten an unborn child's health?

ARISE Foundation, Order Toll-Free: 1-888-680-6100, Copyright © 1996-2009

ASSESSMENT

Name: _____   Date: _____

Circle the correct answer for each statement.

1. If a woman thinks she's pregnant:
    a.   she should see her doctor at once
    b.   she should buy maternity clothes
    c.   she should go out and have a drink
    d.   all of the above

2. Some symptoms of pregnancy include:
    a.   headaches
    b.   cramps
    c.   nausea
    d.   all of the above

3. A baby can be delivered:
    a.   by mail
    b.   vaginally
    c.   by C-section
    d.   both b and c are correct

4. A healthy snack for a pregnant woman is:
    a.   cheese
    b.   carrot sticks
    c.   low-fat yogurt
    d.   all of the above

5. A good exercise for expectant mothers is:
    a.   swimming
    b.   running a marathon
    c.   rollerblading
    d.   high-impact aerobics

Go to www.ariselife-skills.org for fresh, vital lessons that connect youth emotionally and socially.

ASSESSMENT (cont.)

Match definitions on the right to correct terms on the left. Write the correct letter on the blank before each word.

6. _____ contractions

7. _____ breast-feeding

8. _____ herpes

9. _____ postpartum

10. _____ C-section

11. _____ folic acid

12. _____ gestational diabetes

13. _____ SIDS

14. _____ caffeine

15. _____ dilation

a. a sexually transmitted disease

b. cut made to a mother's abdomen to deliver the baby

c. mineral that helps prevent birth defects

d. found in coffee, tea, soft drinks, and certain medications; may cause birth defects

e. help a woman's body push out a baby

f. may develop during pregnancy; can be controlled by diet

g. opening of the cervix during labor

h. period of time following a birth

i. Sudden Infant Death Syndrome

j. the most natural way to feed an infant

SPROUTS:

SECTION TWO

MENTAL DEVELOPMENT

LEARNER'S WORKSHEETS

Children are likely to live up to what you believe of them.
— Lady Bird Johnson

www.ariselife-skills.org

Mind Power

The majority of what we learn is obtained before we graduate from elementary school.

Forty percent of everything we know is acquired by age four.

We learn 80 percent of what we will ever understand by age eight.

Stimulating (exciting) a child's senses changes the size and structure of his brain. It even alters how it works.

According to a scientific study, 60 to 65 percent of a youngster's working vocabulary is acquired by age three.

ARISE Foundation. Order Toll-Free: 1-888-680-6100, Copyright © 1996-2009

MENTAL DEVELOPMENT TABLE

NEWBORN

Day one:	Listens and is alert
Day three:	Responds when spoken to
Day nine:	Eyes move to sound
Day 14:	Recognizes his mother
Day 18:	Makes sounds and turns his head
Day 24:	Mouth moves when mother speaks

12 WEEKS

Your baby begins to understand his body. He looks at and moves his fingers. He will respond to conversation with nods, smiles, mouth movements, noises, and squeals.

Activity:

Act out nursery rhymes with your child by using dramatic expressions.

24 WEEKS

Your infant makes attention-seeking noises. He will smile at a mirror and blow bubbles.

Activity:

Have your child drop an object; then give it back to him.
Push a ball toward your little one, showing him how it rolls.

ONE YEAR

Your baby knows about kissing and shows many emotions. He will pick up a toy and hand it to you, or he says a few meaningful words. He may recognize an object in a book and point to it.

Activity:

Talk about what you're doing while you perform it, such as putting on clothes.
Help your child learn about animals and sounds they make.

Go to www.ariselife-skills.org for fresh, vital lessons that connect youth emotionally and socially.

MENTAL DEVELOPMENT TABLE (cont.)

18 MONTHS

Your toddler can recognize some items on a page and will point to them if you say their names. He will imitate your actions. He can complete a one-direction request.

Activity:

Encourage learning by doing things over and over. Introduce simple shapes and repeat words.

TWO YEARS

Your child has an increasing vocabulary of the names of objects. He can perform difficult orders and will recognize something previously played with. He will begin to talk and ask questions.

Activity:

Help him use simple tools, such as a shovel, hammer, crayons.
Frequently look at picture books with your child.

THREE YEARS

Your toddler asks a lot of questions. He can count to 10 and build with blocks. He prefers real-life games.

Activity

Work on your youngster's memory by reminding him what you did before.
Make up stories with your child as the main character. Help your little one make simple decisions.

ARISE Foundation, Order Toll-Free: 1-888-680-6100, Copyright © 1996-2009

A SMARTER BABY

Choose an age from newborn to three years old and write it in the box. Next, write a plan of how you could give a child mental stimulation appropriate for this age. For these purposes, don't worry about spelling and grammar. Just do the best you can.

☐ Age

_____

_____

_____

_____

_____

_____

_____

Go to www.ariselife-skills.org for fresh, vital lessons that connect youth emotionally and socially.

BABY TALK

In the spaces below, fill in what parents could be saying to accompany an activity. The first one has been done as an example. For these purposes, don't worry about grammar and spelling. Just do the best you can. The main idea is for you to participate.

Changing baby's diaper

"Now we are going to change your diaper. We need to take the wet one off and slip a dry one on. Let's put your legs up. You're smiling. I like it when you grin. Are you happy to be getting a dry diaper?"

Getting baby dressed

_____

_____

_____

Giving an infant his bath

_____

_____

_____

Feeding a child

_____

_____

_____

ARISE Foundation, Order Toll-Free: 1-888-680-6100, Copyright © 1996-2009

SAFE SPACE

Draw a picture of your child's physical space, where he spends most of his time. Show how it is kept safe while still allowing the little one freedom to move around, then describe it below. Not all of us are born artists. Do the best you can to satisfy yourself.

Go to www.ariselife-skills.org for fresh, vital lessons that connect youth emotionally and socially.

WAYS TO TREAT YOUR CHILD

Read each statement. Place a "P" in the space if a behavior is proper or an "I" if it is improper.

_____ There is a lot of face-to-face interaction with your child.

_____ Talk in a pleasant, soothing voice, use simple language, and look into your baby's eyes.

_____ Move your infant around with no talking.

_____ You are rough or ignore your child's responses

_____ Respond quickly to your infant's cries.

_____ Expect your baby to entertain himself.

_____ Praise your child for his accomplishments.

_____ Do not allow your infant to touch others or force him to play when he is not interested in doing so.

_____ Frequently participate in games with your toddler when he is responsive to play.

_____ Never provide your infant with an opportunity to see himself in a mirror.

_____ Read short stories and poems to your child every chance you get.

ARISE Foundation. Order Toll-Free: 1-888-680-6100, Copyright © 1996-2009

MAKING CHOICES

Change the following general choices to more specific ones. For these purposes, don't worry about grammar and spelling. Just do the best you can. The main idea is for you to participate.

What kind of socks do you want to wear? _____

_____

What book would you like to read?_____

_____

What movie do you want to watch? _____

_____

What would you like for lunch? _____

_____

What would you like to wear today?

_____

_____

FINGER PLAYS

(As you say each line, gently wiggle your child's toe. As you speak the last line, tickle your little one gently.)

This little piggy went to market,
This little piggy stayed home,
This little piggy had roast beef,
This little piggy had none,
This little piggy cried "wee, wee,wee" all the way home.

Round and round the garden like a teddy bear
(Draw circles on your child's hand.)
One step,
Two steps,
(Crawl your fingers up his arm.)
Tickle under there.
(Tickle infant under the arm.)

Pat-a-cake, pat-a-cake, bakers man,
(Clap hands.)
Bake me a cake as fast as you can,
Roll it and pull it and mark it with a "B,"
(Dramatic play rolling and marking.)
Throw it in the oven for baby and me.
(Throw your arms out.)

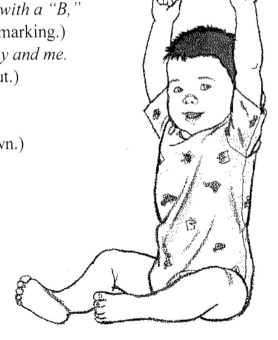

(Hold hands and walk in a circle; on the last line, sit down.)
Ring around the rosie,
Pocket full of posies,
Ashes, ashes, we all fall down.

ARISE Foundation Order Toll-Free: 1-888-680-6100, Copyright © 1996-2009

COMPLETE THE RHYME

Unscramble words to complete each nursery rhyme.

Little Miss Muffet, sat on a tuffet ENATIG
her curds and whey. Along came a SDEPIR
and sat down beside her and ERIGHTFEND
Miss Muffet away.

_____

_____

_____

Little Boy Blue, come blow your OHNR,
the SEEPH are in the meadow, the WOCS
in the corn. Where's the TTLLIE boy who looks
after the sheep? He's under the HASTCYAK
fast asleep.

_____

_____

_____

_____

_____

Hey, diddle diddle, the TAC and the fiddle,
the OCW jumped over the NMOO.
The little dog LGHEDAU to see such sport
and the HDIS ran away with the spoon.

_____

_____

_____

_____

Little Bo Peep has lost her SPHEE
and doesn't know where to find them.
Leave them alone and they'll come home, GIGNDRGA
their tails BHINED them.

_____

_____

_____

Go to www.ariselife-skills.org for fresh, vital lessons that connect youth emotionally and socially.

WORD BANK

moon	little	sheep (used twice)	dragging	cat
eating	behind	laughed	haystack	spider
cows	frightened	horn	cow	dish

DRESS-UP TRUNK

List those items you have at home to be placed in a dress-up trunk. For these purposes, don't worry about grammar and spelling. Just do the best you can. The main idea is for you to participate.

_____

_____

_____

_____

_____

_____

_____

_____

_____

_____

_____

Do It Yourself

Think of ways you can plan real-life experiences for young children. The first two have been done as an example. For these purposes, don't worry about grammar and spelling. Just do the best you can. The main idea is for you to participate.

Setting the table: Have a three year old help set the table each night.

Cleaning clothes: Give youngsters a bucket of water with soap and let them wash their doll's clothes. Remember to supervise your child at all times.

Pouring milk or juice:

_____

_____

Sorting laundry:

_____

_____

Doing dishes:

_____

_____

Sweeping floors:

_____

_____

Cleaning their room:

_____

_____

Go to www.ariselife-skills.org for fresh, vital lessons that connect youth emotionally and socially.

TEACH A NEW SKILL

Select a brand-new skill to teach a young child. Divide it into small steps and write down each one. Read them to a partner. Have him do only what is said in the instructions. Check on how you broke down the task by how well the other person was able to perform them. For these purposes, don't worry about grammar and spelling. Just do the best you can. The main idea is for you to participate.

_____

_____

_____

_____

_____

_____

_____

ARISE Foundation Order Toll-Free: 1-888-680-6100, Copyright © 1996-2009

COOKING WITH KIDS

Step by step, describe how all kitchen appliances work (toaster, stove) and why it's so important to be careful around them.

Before any cooking activity, make sure the child washes his hands.

Explain why youngsters should not walk around with utensils or lick them if they are going to be put back into a group dish. Also tell them why eating food off the floor is not healthy.

Teach little ones to ask permission before tasting something because it may be hot.

Gather all materials you need before your lesson begins so no child will be left unsupervised.

REMEMBER THESE KITCHEN SAFETY TIPS:

- Turn off all burners when cooking has been completed.
- Stirring materials, like spoons, should never be left in the pot while food cooks.
- The oven must never be used for any purpose other than cooking.
- Don't allow pot handles to hang over the edge of the stove.
- In case of burns, don't use butter or grease; they hold in heat, making the injury worse.
- Run cold water on minor burns; anything else may need immediate medical attention.

DAILY LIFE LEARNING

Read each daily-life situation and decide how you could teach at least three categories through an activity. The first one has been done as an example. For these purposes, don't worry about grammar and spelling. Just do the best you can. The main idea is for you to participate.

Categories: Language   Socializing   Counting
                    Listening   Color

Situations:

1. **Going for a walk**
    Color: naming the color of cars
    Counting: walking around and counting objects like trees
    Socializing: saying hello to people you see

2. **Traveling in a car**

    _____
    _____
    _____
    _____

3. **Going to the grocery store**

    _____
    _____
    _____
    _____

4. **Cleaning house**

    _____
    _____
    _____

5. **Write your own idea here**

    _____
    _____
    _____

KIDS AND TV

Children watch an average of 21 to 27 hours of TV per week.

By the time today's little one reaches age 70, he will have spent seven to 10 years of his life facing a TV.

The average preschool and school-age child who sees two to four hours of noneducational TV per day will have witnessed at least 8,000 murders and more than 100,000 other acts of violence by the time he completes elementary school. *This is not a good thing!*

Go to www.ariselife-skills.org for fresh, vital lessons that connect youth emotionally and socially.

QUALITY TELEVISION

The Big Comfy Couch   *Sesame Street*
Mr. Rogers' Neighborhood   *Lamb Chop's Playhouse*
Barney   *Reading Rainbow*
Wishbone   *Magic School Bus*

I selected _____.

It was on from _____ to _____ .

The main characters were _____.

The message of this program was _____

_____.

I think children would learn from this TV show because _____

_____.

My favorite part was _____.

The segment I didn't like was _____.

I think this would be a good program for small children to watch
because_____

_____.

ARISE Foundation, Order Toll-Free: 1-888-680-6100, Copyright © 1996-2009

CHOOSING TV PROGRAMS

Complete this worksheet based on the TV show you watched and did a report on.

Do you respect the program? (You should believe in the show's general message and values.)

_____

Are there different types of children (male, female, short, tall) on the show? _____

How do creators of the program view youngsters? (Be sure they treat little ones as learners.)

_____

_____

Does the show mention any important issues to children (language, counting, self-esteem, safety)?

_____

Go to www.ariselife-skills.org for fresh, vital lessons that connect youth emotionally and socially.

TV Tips Secret Code

Use the clues below to crack the secret code. For example, ✌ stands for A, and 👌 stands for B. 👇✌✡ would represent the word "day."

ARISE Foundation, Order Toll-Free: 1-888-680-6100, Copyright © 1996-2009

KEY TIPS

Review the following as a group:

1. Stimulate your child's mind with sounds, sights, and smells.

2. Allow your little one a safe area to play in and move around freely.

3. Help kids learn to make decisions by keeping choices simple.

4. Teach youngsters plays, songs, poems, and rhymes; it does wonders for their language skills.

5. Watch quality educational TV programs with your children. *Sesame Street, Reading Rainbow,* and *Lamb Chop's Playhouse* are all great examples.

Go to www.ariselife-skills.org for fresh, vital lessons that connect youth emotionally and socially.

Chapter 5 Quiz: Your Child's Mental Development

Name: _____   Date: _____

Circle the correct answer for each statement.

1. Children learn much through:
   a.   movements   b.   sights
   c.   sounds   d.   all of the above

2. Kids must be allowed to make ____ decisions:
   a.   all of their own   b.   none of their own
   c.   some easy   d.   none of the above

3. If a child does not want to try a new activity, parents should:
   a.   not force him   b.   make him do it anyway
   c.   punish the youngster   d.   both b and c are correct

4. Placing a TV set in a child's room:
   a.   is not a good idea   b.   is a great idea
   c.   saves electricity   d.   none of the above

5. By age eight, children already know _____ of everything they will ever learn.
   a.   10 percent   b.   25 percent
   c.   80 percent   d.   none of the above

Suitable Toys and Activities

Newborn

For the first few weeks, a newborn baby needs physical contact, gentle voices, and smiling faces. The child also requires toys to excite all five senses. Suitable playthings for an infant under one year of age are those with bright colors, interesting shapes, and those which make noise.

12 Weeks

Toys to swat, kick, and hold a mobile
Squeaking or sucking items
Plastic-coated photographs
Baby mirrors
Soft playthings like balls

Six Months

Picture books (hard or plastic pages)
Activity center
Bath toys
Things to bang
Balls
Cloth books
Movable playthings
Large soft blocks

Go to www.ariselife-skills.org for fresh, vital lessons that connect youth emotionally and socially.

SUITABLE TOYS AND ACTIVITIES (cont.)

ONE YEAR
Picture books
Sand
Telephone
Music box or toys

18 MONTHS
Music for dancing
Push-along toys
Crayons and paper
Blocks and other stacking playthings
Vehicles

TWO YEARS
Ball
Objects to match and sort
Construction blocks
Dolls
Hammering toys

THREE YEARS
Puzzles
Simple games with large pieces
Dress-up toys
Tape player

ARISE Foundation, Order Toll-Free: 1-888-680-6100, Copyright © 1996-2009

CHOOSE THE APPROPRIATE TOY

Refer to worksheet pages 44 and 45 to write the correct age group under each object.

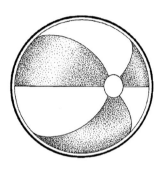

_____

_____

_____

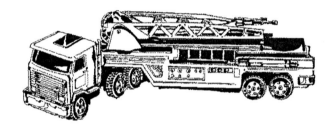

_____

_____

_____

_____

TOYS AROUND THE HOUSE

List items in each of the rooms below that could be safe toys for young children. The first object has been done as an example.

Kitchen:
Pots and pans

_____

_____

_____

Bathroom:
Washcloth

_____

_____

_____

_____

Bedroom:
Rolled-up sock

_____

_____

_____

_____

ARISE Foundation, Order Toll-Free: 1-888-680-6100, Copyright © 1996-2009

Is It Safe?

Read each description and place a check mark next to good toys.

_____ Stuffed animal with loose button eyes

_____ Metal truck with a broken hood

_____ Pull-toy with long string

_____ Mobile with thick plastic cords and an age recommendation of newborn to three months

_____ Washable rag doll with painted face

_____ Truck coated in lead-based paint

_____ Set of marbles

_____ Tricycle

Go to www.ariselife-skills.org for fresh, vital lessons that connect youth emotionally and socially.

CREATE A STORY

Write a story in which a child — star of the tale — encounters a problem and solves it. For these purposes, don't worry about grammar and spelling. Just do the best you can. The main idea is for you to participate.

_____

_____

_____

_____

_____

_____

_____

_____

_____

_____

ARISE Foundation, Order Toll-Free: 1-888-680-6100, Copyright © 1996-2009

TOYS AND BOOKS CROSSWORD PUZZLE

Use clues and word bank below to solve the crossword puzzle.

ACROSS

1. *The* _____ *Billy Goats Gruff* is a good story for kids.
4. Blow _____ with your child... it's fun!
7. Read a bedtime _____ to your little one.
9. Nonwashable toys may contain many _____.
10. Soft, large _____ are good playthings for small children.

DOWN

2. Some items around the _____ can be good toys for youngsters.
3. Avoid those with sharp _____.
5. Do not buy toys with long _____ attached.
6. Playthings with small _____ can cause a child to choke.
8. You can make homemade _____ using flour.

Word Bank			
balls	clay	edges	three
bubbles	house	story	strings
germs	parts		

Go to www.ariselife-skills.org for fresh, vital lessons that connect youth emotionally and socially.

TOYS AND BOOKS
CROSSWORD PUZZLE (CONT.)

ARISE Foundation, Order Toll-Free: 1-888-680-6100, Copyright © 1996-2009

KEY TIPS

Review the following as a group:

1. Select age-appropriate toys for little ones.

2. Have fun with your child; create art materials and playthings together by using household items.

3. Beware: toys cause thousands of injuries to children each year.

4. Give your youngster a precious gift: the love of reading. Share stories and books with him as often as possible.

5. Take your little one to the library. There are countless activities available there, including movies, arts and crafts, and story time for kids.

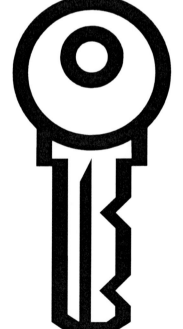

CHAPTER 6 QUIZ: TOYS AND BOOKS

Name: _____   Date: _____

Circle the correct answer for each statement.

1. A safe toy for a baby is a:
    a. metal truck
    b. big, soft ball
    c. doll with a long pull string
    d. all of the above

2. When buying toys for a young child, parents should look for the following:
    a. no small pieces
    b. no sharp edges
    c. how washable it is
    d. all of the above

3. At the library, people can:
    a. sing and dance
    b. run around and yell
    c. check out books and videos
    d. all of the above

4. A household item safe for youngsters to play with is a:
    a. washcloth
    b. knife
    c. match
    d. none of the above

5. To allow a child to explore her environment, parents should:
    a. strap her tightly in her stroller
    b. keep her in a crib all day
    c. allow her to move around as much as possible
    d. none of the above

ARISE Foundation, Order Toll-Free: 1-888-680-6100, Copyright © 1996-2009

POEMS

Read the poems as a group.

Mother to Son
by Langston Hughes

Well, son, I'll tell you:
Life for me ain't been no crystal stair.
It's had tacks in it
And splinters,
And boards torn up,
And places with no carpet on the floor —
Bare.
But all the time
I'se been a-climbin' on
And reachin' landin's,
And turnin' corners,
And sometimes goin' in the dark
Where there ain't been no light.
So boy, don't you turn back.
Don't you set down on the steps
'Cause you find it's kinder hard.
Don't you fall now,
For I'se still goin', honey,
I'se still climbin',
And life for me ain't been
no crystal stair.

Go to www.ariselife-skills.org for fresh, vital lessons that connect youth emotionally and socially.

POEMS (cont.)

Roots and Wings — The Greatest Gifts We Can Give Our Children
by Roger A. Desmarais, Ph.D.
(Excerpts)

Roots
A solid place from which to begin
Based on love, discipline,
Opportunities, support,
Encouragement to go the extra mile
And the resources to do so,
An environment of family and friends.

Wings
The courage and motivation
To try one's flight,
To go where you've never been before,
To reach out and touch
A whole new world of the mind,
Feelings, insights, ideas, and friends...

ARISE Foundation, Order Toll-Free: 1-888-680-6100, Copyright © 1996-2009

POEMS (cont.)

Children, Children Everywhere
Anonymous

Children, children everywhere,
Children dark and children fair,
Children of all shapes and sizes,
Children springing odd surprises,
Children chasing, running races,
Children laughing, making faces,
Children cooking mud for dinner,
Children, every one a winner.

Children jumping, children wiggling,
Children grumping, children giggling,
Children singing, sneezing, weeping,
Children sometimes even sleeping,
Children giving children hugs,
Children chewing worms and bugs,
Children in their parents' hair,
Children, children everywhere.

Go to www.ariselife-skills.org for fresh, vital lessons that connect youth emotionally and socially.

MY OWN POEM

Below, write a poem for the child you may have some day. For these purposes, don't worry about grammar and spelling. Just do the best you can. The main idea is for you to participate.

_____

_____

_____

_____

_____

_____

_____

_____

_____

_____

POETRY SECRET CODE

Use the clues below to crack the secret code. For example, 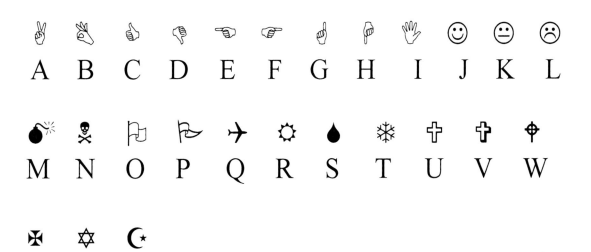 stands for A, and stands for B. would represent the word "day."

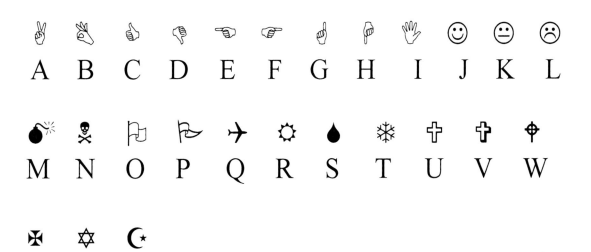

A	B	C	D	E	F	G	H	I	J	K	L

M	N	O	P	Q	R	S	T	U	V	W

X	Y	Z

S H A R E   S O M E   P O E T R Y   W I T H

Y O U R   C H I L D .

KEY TIPS

Review the following with learners:

1. Read some poetry with your little one; it's a rewarding experience.

2. Write a poem for your child and share it with him at bedtime.

3. There are many books available for youngsters. Buy some (or check them out at the library) and read one poem per day to your little sprout.

ARISE Foundation, Order Toll-Free: 1-888-680-6100, Copyright © 1996-2009

CHAPTER 7 QUIZ: POETRY

Name: _____   Date: _____

Circle the correct answer for each statement.

1. Reading poetry can be a good experience for:
    a. adults   b. children
    c. pets   d. both a and b are correct

2. When a child is two years old, he may be allowed to watch TV for:
    a. as long as he wants   b. one hour per day
    c. five hours per day   d. none of the above

3. Sharing poems with a youngster is:
    a. a good way to spend quality time   b. a waste of time
    c. boring   d. none of the above

4. Children whose parents often read to them:
    a. learn to love reading   b. hate books
    c. don't like the library   d. both b and c are correct

5. Poetry can be enjoyed by:
    a. only adults   b. only children
    c. everyone   d. none of the above

ROLE CARD: HOST

"Good morning (afternoon.) Welcome to our special segment on 'Turbocharging Your Child's Mind.' We're here today to talk about how parents can help expand their youngster's imagination and mental skills."

We have with us a distinguished panel of guests, including:

Peter Galinski, a counselor;
Erin, mother of a five-year-old girl;
Michelle, Erin's daughter;
and **Edmund Nichols**, a teacher and poet."

"Please welcome our panelists to the show."

"We're here today to discuss the important role parents play in their child's mental development. By stimulating a little one's senses and experiencing new activities together, mom and dad can expand their children's abilities to learn, understand, and create."

"In fact, youngsters who are read to by their parents are more likely to develop a larger vocabulary and better writing skills than kids who are not read to often. This says a lot about how families can influence their children's learning capacity."

"I'll begin today by introducing Peter Galinski, a counselor at a local elementary school. Mr. Galinski, explain to us what your job has taught you about children and how they learn."

(Peter Galinski responds)

"Next, I'd like to introduce Erin. She says because she reads to her daughter, Michelle now has better language skills than other kids her age. Erin, what made you come to this conclusion?"

(Erin responds)

ARISE Foundation, Order Toll-Free: 1-888-680-6100, Copyright © 1996-2009

ROLE CARD: HOST

(Once Erin has responded, ask if there are any concerns from the audience. Select one or two volunteers who have their hands raised to ask questions of the panel.)

"Please welcome Michelle, Erin's daughter. Michelle, tell us: Why do you enjoy reading so much? Does your mommy take you to the library often?"

(Michelle speaks)

"Finally, I'd like to welcome Mr. Edmund Nichols to the show. Mr. Nichols is a fifth-grade teacher who writes children's poetry in his spare time. Mr. Nichols, why do you feel parents should share poetry with their youngsters?"

(Edmund Nichols speaks)

(Once Edmund Nichols finishes, go through the audience and select those members with role cards to ask questions. Give the panel a chance to answer. If time permits, ask if there is anyone else with concerns regarding nurturing or loving a child.
Again, allow panelists to answer.)

"Thanks for joining us today. Remember to take your child to the library. It's a great place for both parents and kids to spend an afternoon!"

Go to www.ariselife-skills.org for fresh, vital lessons that connect youth emotionally and socially.

ROLE CARD: PETER GALINSKI

You are a counselor at a local elementary school. Through years of experience, you've discovered that children who are read to and exposed to new, exciting learning activities, develop advanced mental and creative skills. You are here to encourage all parents to become involved with their kids' learning processes and want to stress the importance of allowing youngsters freedom to safely move about and discover things on their own. You also want to remind parents not all toys and games are good for their little ones; those with long strings, loose pieces, and sharp edges often lead to serious (even deadly) injuries.

You also want moms and dads to understand infants go through different stages of development and parents must be careful in choosing age-appropriate toys and activities for their child.

ARISE Foundation, Order Toll-Free: 1-888-680-6100, Copyright © 1996-2009

ROLE CARD: ERIN

You are the mother of a five-year-old daughter, Michelle. Since she was a baby, you have read to her, watched TV programs together, and created art projects at home. Michelle is a very bright child, and you believe your effort and attention is in large part the reason for this. Michelle has a large vocabulary and excellent reading skills. Her teacher has told you she is one of the best artists in her class. You and Michelle often go to the library and have discovered many wonderful ways to spend the day there. Both of you have so much fun together and you want to share your secret of success with other parents.

Go to www.ariselife-skills.org for fresh, vital lessons that connect youth emotionally and socially.

ROLE CARD: MICHELLE

You are Erin's five-year-old daughter, a happy, creative child who reads very well and loves to draw and paint. Your kindergarten teacher says you are a really smart girl and is always praising your artwork. You love spending time with your mom because she always comes up with fun things to do. You often watch TV together and your favorite show is *Sesame Street*.

Go to www.ariselife-skills.org for fresh, vital lessons that connect youth emotionally and socially.

ARISE Foundation, Order Toll-Free: 1-888-680-6100, Copyright © 1996-2009

ROLE CARD: EDMUND NICHOLS

You are a fifth-grade teacher who writes children's poems in your spare time. You believe it is important to share art activities with a child and think poetry is a great way to develop a youngster's reading, writing, and creative skills. You are here to encourage parents to play a larger role in their little one's mental development by: writing stories, poems, and songs together; attending local children's museums; watching educational TV shows; and enjoying games as a family.

Go to www.ariselife-skills.org for fresh, vital lessons that connect youth emotionally and socially.

AUDIENCE CARDS

- -

What's so important about reading to your youngsters? Does it really make a difference?

- -

Why is the library a good place to take your children?

- -

Are all TV shows for little ones the same? Why should parents sit and watch TV with their young ones?

- -

ARISE Foundation, Order Toll-Free: 1-888-680-6100, Copyright © 1996-2009

ASSESSMENT

Name: _____   Date: _____

Circle the correct answer for each statement.

1. The following is a poor way to treat a child:
    a.   giving a baby a lot of kisses   b.   ignoring a child's cries
    c.   playing with a toddler   d.   none of the above

2. A good game for young children is:
    a.   pat-a-cake   b.   ring around the rosie
    c.   this little piggy   d.   all of the above

3. Youngsters can help around the house by:
    a.   sweeping floors   b.   ironing clothes
    c.   cleaning toilets   d.   all of the above

4. A great TV show for kids is:
    a.   *Mr. Roger's Neighborhood*   b.   *Sesame Street*
    c.   *Melrose Place*   d.   both a and b are correct

5. When choosing toys for children, parents should beware of:
    a.   sharp corners   b.   small pieces
    c.   long strings   d.   all of the above

ASSESSMENT (cont.)

Match definitions on the right correct with terms on the left. Write the correct letter in the blank before each word.

6. _____ Mind power

    a. *The Three Little Pigs and Little Red Riding Hood* are good examples of these.

7. _____ Poetry

    b. A child must be allowed to make simple ones.

8. _____ Movements

    c. *Reading Rainbow and Lamb Chop's Playhouse* are good examples of these.

9. _____ Choices

    d. Growing up in an exciting environment will stimulate this.

10. _____ Bedtime stories

    e. allow a child to explore her world.

11. _____ Kids' TV shows

    f. is a household object safe for kids to play with.

12. _____ A pot or pan

    g. is not just written for adults; children can enjoy this, too.

Go to www.ariselife-skills.org for fresh, vital lessons that connect youth emotionally and socially.

ARISE Foundation, Order Toll-Free: 1-888-680-6100, Copyright © 1996-2009

SPROUTS:

SECTIONS ONE AND TWO

WORKSHEET
ANSWERS

www.ariselife-skills.org

WORKSHEET ANSWERS SECTION ONE

Substance Abuse: Caffeine (Word Match), Worksheet: *Page 79* **Learner's Workbook:** *Page 33*
1. D   2. A   3. E   4. F 5. G   6. C   7. B

Substance Abuse: Drugs, Worksheet: *Page 83* **Learner's Workbook:** *Page 37*

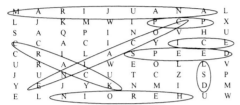

Foods to Avoid Crossword Puzzle, Worksheet: *Pages 89-90* **Learner's Workbook:** *Pages 43-44*

ACROSS		DOWN	
1.	fried foods	2.	ice cream
5.	cookies	3.	fruit juice
6.	canned fruits	4.	sugar
7.	butter		
8.	chips		

Food Guide (Matching Foods), Worksheet: *Page 92* **Learner's Workbook:** *Page 46*
1.D   2.G   3.F   4.B   5.A   6.C   7.E

Delivery Definitions, Worksheet: *Page 100* **Learner's Workbook:** *Page 54*
1. B   2. D   3. E   4.C   5.A 6. G   7.H   8. F

Pregnancy Word Search, Worksheet: *Page 101* **Learner's Workbook:** *Page 55*
1. anesthetic	2. dilation	3. cervix	4. uterus
5. contraction	6. crowning		

Scrambled Delivery, Worksheet: *Page 102* **Learner's Workbook:** *Page 56*
1. effacement	2. amniotic fluid	3. APGAR score	4. postpartum	5. hemorrhoids
6. placenta	7. episiotomy	8. presentation	9. hormones	10. induced labor

Order of Delivery, Worksheet: *Page 111* **Learner's Workbook:** *Page 65*
1.   Baby's head will emerge and a nurse will suction the baby's mouth.
2.   Labor room attendant will wipe off newborn and clear the airways.
3.   Infant will be placed on mother's abdomen to be held, admired, and cuddled.
4.   A nurse may give the baby an APGAR test.
5.   After first round of testing, the doctor cuts umbilical cord. The child is then moved to another table, rubbed down with a towel, weighed, footprinted, given an ID bracelet, and wrapped in a blanket.
6.   Eye drops are usually given to prevent infection.
7.   Placenta is withdrawn, uterine cavity is examined and cleaned.
8.   Newborn is returned to the mother's arms.
9.   Mom is cleaned up and stitched if an episiotomy was performed.

Go to www.ariselife-skills.org for fresh, vital lessons that connect youth emotionally and socially.

ARISE Foundation, Order Toll-Free: 1-888-680-6100, Copyright © 1996-2009

WORKSHEET ANSWERS SECTION ONE (cont.)

Postpartum Misconceptions, Worksheet: *Page 115* **Learner's Workbook:** *Page 69*
After the infant is cleaned up, he will look as beautiful as the picture on a baby-food jar.
FALSE: The newborn's head may be large or misshapen after a snug fit through the pelvis. He may also have a white, waxy covering on his skin. This is called "vernix caseosa" and it protects the baby's skin during pregnancy. Child might have puffy eyes, swollen genitals, and skin rashes or blotches; however, all of these will disappear in a short period of time.

After giving birth, a woman quickly loses all the weight she gained during pregnancy.
FALSE: She will not have her prepregnancy body back for a while. This takes time, a healthy diet, and exercise to lose weight and tone up muscles (especially the abdominal muscles). It's very rare you look the same as before pregnancy.

New mothers are so happy with their new babies that nothing else matters.
FALSE: Sometime during the first five days after a baby's birth, a new mother may experience temporary depression. She may find herself crying often for no apparent reason. This is natural and will usually pass. If it lasts longer than five days (which is rare), call a doctor.

New mothers will be in some pain for awhile and need help with things such as housework and caring for baby.
TRUE: Getting help from a partner, parents, hospital home-visit nurse, friends, or community members is almost essential. Giving birth is hard work and getting help will give the new mom time to take care of her child.

Since breast-feeding is natural, it is easy to do.
FALSE: The baby's best nutrition is breast milk; however, breast-feeding is a skill that must be learned by both woman and infant. New mothers should ask for help from nurses in the hospital.

If a woman bleeds after giving birth and returning home, she should call the doctor immediately.
FALSE: Bloody vaginal discharge called "lochea" is normal. It may sometimes be heavier than the normal menstrual period; however, if a woman experiences bleeding that soaks more than one pad per hour for more than a few hours, she should have someone take her to the emergency room if she's unable to immediately contact her doctor.

Only rotten parents get frustrated with their new baby.
FALSE: Many mothers and fathers feel frustration toward their infant when he's crying or wakes up in the middle of the night, especially when they are unsure about what to do. The best thing a new mom can do is try to relax and ask for help from her partner, friends, or parents. Parents must never turn their temper to physically abusing a child. If you feel frustrated, call your doctor and discuss your fears and concerns.

Baby at Home Crossword Puzzle, Worksheet: *Pages 127-128* **Learner's Workbook:** *Pages 81-82*

Across	Down	
5. manage	1. time	4. changes
7. organized	2. support	6. weight
8. table	3. natural	

WORKSHEET ANSWERS SECTION TWO

Complete the Rhyme, Worksheet: *Page 151* **Learner's Workbook:** *Page 105*

eating	horn	cat	sheep
spider	sheep, cows	cow, moon	dragging
frightened	little	laughed	behind
	haystack	dish	

TV Tips Secret Code, Worksheet: *Page 160* **Learner's Workbook:** *Page 114*
Do not place a TV set in your child's room. Help your child select TV programs.

Toys and Books Crossword Puzzle, Worksheet: *Pages 169-170* **Learner's Workbook:** *Pages 123-124*

ACROSS	DOWN
1. three	2. house
4. bubbles	3. edges
7. story	5. strings
9. germs	6. parts
10. balls	8. clay

Poetry Secret Code, Worksheet: *Page 177* **Learner's Workbook:** *Page 131*
Share some poetry with your child.

ARISE Foundation, Order Toll-Free: 1-888-680-6100, Copyright © 1996-2009

SPROUTS:

SECTIONS ONE AND TWO

QUIZ AND ASSESSMENT ANSWERS

www.ariselife-skills.org

SECTION ONE QUIZ ANSWERS

Chapter 1:
1. D 2. B 3. C 4. D 5. B

Chapter 2:
1. D 2. C 3. B 4. D 5. D

Chapter 3:
1. C 2. C 3. D 4. A 5. D

SECTION TWO QUIZ ANSWERS

Chapter 1:
1. D 2. C 3. A 4. A 5. C

Chapter 2:
1. B 2. D 3. C 4. A 5. C

Chapter 3:
1. D 2. B 3. A 4. A 5. C

SECTION ONE ASSESSMENT ANSWERS

Multiple Choice		**Matching**			
1.	A	6.	E	11.	C
2.	D	7.	J	12.	F
3.	D	8.	A	13.	I
4.	D	9.	H	14.	D
5.	A	10.	B	15.	G

SECTION TWO ASSESSMENT ANSWERS

Multiple Choice		**Matching**			
1.	B	6.	D	11.	C
2.	D	7.	G	12.	F
3.	A	8.	E		
4.	D	9.	B		
5.	D	10.	A		

Rev: 5/2008

ARISE Foundation, Order Toll-Free: 1-888-680-6100, Copyright © 1996-2009